DIRECT APPROACH

CHRISTIAN DRAMA FOR YOUNG PEOPLE

ANNE COLLINS

First published in 1998 by
KEVIN MAYHEW LTD
Rattlesden
Bury St Edmunds
Suffolk IP30 0SZ

© 1998 Anne Collins

The right of Anne Collins to be identified as the author
of this work has been asserted by her in accordance
with the Copyright, Designs and Patents Act 1988.

The scripts within this book may be photocopied by the organisation
which purchases this copy without copyright infringement,
provided they are used for the purpose for which they are intended.
Reproduction of any of the contents of this book for commercial purposes
is subject to the usual copyright restrictions.

No other part of this publication may be reproduced,
stored in a retrieval system, or transmitted, in any form or by any means,
electronic, mechanical, photocopying, recording or otherwise,
without the prior written permission of the publisher.

All rights reserved.

0 1 2 3 4 5 6 7 8 9

ISBN 1 84003 229 4
Catalogue No 1500215

Cover illustration by Kirstie Whiteford
Cover design by Jaquetta Sergeant
Edited by David Gatward
Printed in Great Britain

Contents

This book is dedicated to the glory of God
and to all Mustard Seeds, past, present and future.

The Kingdom of Heaven is like this.
A man takes a mustard seed and sows it in his field.
It is the smallest of all seeds, but when it grows up,
it is the biggest of all plants. It becomes a tree,
so that birds come and make their nests in its branches.
Matthew 13:31-32

I assure you that if you have faith as big as a mustard seed,
you can say to this hill, 'Go from here to there!' and it will go.
You could do anything.
Matthew 17:20

Also by Anne Collins:
Rock Solid, A foundation course in youth drama for worship.

Acknowledgements

This book is dedicated firstly to the glory of God, and secondly to all the Mustard Seeds scattered around England and indeed the world, especially South Africa. Thirdly it is a way of thanking all those who ever befriended us, watered us, fed us, pruned us, and cared for us over the years in Christian love, and all the friends from Theatre Church and St. Andrew's in Bolton. I remember especially our Christian friends in Devon and Cornwall who put up with 'Mustard Seed Mania' for several summers without complaint, fed us with wise words of fellowship (and pavlova), and with so much love. I thank, too, Darren, Helen, Fiona and Mark, who gave up so much of their time to help Mustard Seed in the early years, and to Dennis and Sally Burton who provided inspirational help. Finally I thank my husband Geoff for his patience and support without which the Seeds would never have been sown.

Introduction

Have you ever wanted to have a go at Drama in Worship? Or try your hand at evangelism and outreach? Or do you just feel that the youngsters in your church would benefit from a different approach to bible study? Do you want to communicate the Word of God in a vital and immediate way? Then read on . . . this book of sketches may be for you.

If you have reservations about your ability to direct drama in worship, worry not! Parallel to the sketches are 'Director's tips', to help even the least experienced person. Normally you only get the sketches and spend ages working out and blocking the moves. These tips should save you time and energy. If you already have experience, then the sketches provide a lively and unusual insight into different stories and issues raised in the bible, and you can ignore the 'tips' if you wish, and develop the sketches and characters in your own way.

These sketches are tried and tested, and were devised and performed originally by Mustard Seed, a Christian Drama Fellowship of young people aged between 12-18 years, working in the North West. They have been performed in a variety of venues of many shapes and sizes, as Street Theatre and as part of worship and outreach. The Seeds are now scattered, and the fruits of their labours remained sitting in files on my shelves. I was prompted to share them, and now hope that they will inspire a new generation of young people and adults, to get out there and communicate the Word of God to new audiences, in a challenging way.

Over the years I have come up against the well meaning, often enthusiastic, but I feel, misguided attitude of, 'Let's do a sketch in the service tomorrow, it'll liven things up, and appeal to the young people'. One hour's preparation, and 'bingo' – it's performed, often with nervousness and embarrassed giggles from the young people, and the distraction of bits of paper clutched in the hand as a 'prop'. It would not be fair to say that these impromptu versions of God's word never communicate, God's message is strong and can be seen glimmering amongst the worst debris, but I do believe that we can do a better job for him! The Lord has given us all so much, and I believe that we should do our very best for him. We would not present an anthem, or choral piece for worship that is sung out of tune, and the same principle applies to Drama in Worship. We must be prepared to work hard to learn the basic skills of good communication, so that we can tell his wonderful story with greater clarity. This isn't about 'performance' but about worship and the offering of ourselves wholly to God in his service.

The other important issue that this attitude to drama in worship masks is that it is a creative process which is not only a learning experience in terms of life skills, but also a very effective way of opening hearts and minds to God, and to others. When handed over to him, with a commitment to the search for his truth, and the determination to work hard, in his name – then impossible and wonderful things can and do happen. It acts as a crucible, into which the Lord can pour his Holy Spirit, and through his Son, lead us and guide us, teach us and restrain us. Without this approach drama can be dangerous, and create mini 'stars', big 'egos' and uncaring attitudes. When this kind of work is pursued through prayer and fellowship, the quiet and shy can express their deep faith and gain confidence, the bold extrovert can learn to make way for others, the strong in faith can hold up the weak, the confident, lead the nervous, and all can love each other and learn together in the name of Jesus.

Taking this way is not easy. It means meeting as a group on a regular basis at least for a reasonable length of time, taking three to six weeks over the preparation of one sketch. It means that ministers and Local Preachers must not expect instant sketches at a moment's notice! It means pooling skills, and exploring

Christian belief with all its difficult questions and immense challenges to our lives. But the reward of communicating that faith in the best way possible, can bring others to God, raise awareness of issues, and challenge the most unlikely people into action for God.

ANNE COLLINS

About the Author

Anne Collins lives in the North of England, and has been a teacher for over thirty years. She is married, with two children, both actors. She has retired from teaching as such, but works as an 'Artist in Schools', bringing her experience in drama skills to staff and pupils. From 1985 until 1993 she directed the Mustard Seed Drama Fellowship (an ecumenical group including young people from all denominations, plus those searching for faith), which appeared twice at MAYC, in the Westminster Central Hall, firstly with sketches similar to those in this book, and secondly with a production of *The Man*, a multimedia rock musical paralleling conditions of the world, with the person of Jesus Christ, and challenging all to 'stand up and be counted' alongside him against injustice, prejudice and cruelty.

She was also involved in Youth Theatre Workshops, writing full-scale productions with a message, such as *Snow Queen* (With God all things are possible), *Pinocchio* (New life is available for all), *Alice* (Be as a little child), creating original nativity scripts for church and school, and, as Head of Drama in a variety of schools, teaching. Her ministry with Mustard Seed included leading services, church weekends, and Drama in Worship courses. From this has arisen her latest project, 'Sowing Seeds', a kind of 'have workshop will travel' idea. She also runs, along with Geoff, her husband, 'Drama Workshop', for young people aged eight upwards, which homes-in on drama skills, builds confidence and creates a good group experience for those involved. She and her husband attend St Andrew's Methodist Church in Bolton.

She hopes that this book, written from her experience, will be of use to those who feel called to communicate God's word through drama, and especially to those who are afraid to make the first move because of a lack of confidence.

Introducing this Book

These seven sketches can be used independently or in conjunction with *Rock Solid, a foundation course in Drama for worship* (Kevin Mayhew Publishers). It is aimed initially at youth groups who wish to present the word of God in a church setting as part of worship, or as an outreach in a variety of situations.

The sketches are arranged with the easier ones first and the most difficult last. They include Director's tips as an aid to leaders who feel that they need support when staging sketches for worship. Each page of script is paralleled with these tips to make the job easier. However, the more experienced director can use them with his/her own directions if desired. They will be most successful and will communicate more if time is taken to prepare and rehearse them.

Bible study of the texts prior to working on them is a vital ingredient leading to their success as communication of God's word within the group, and to the audiences who will share the final presentations. (There are suggestions for their development, within the Director's tips which will enable a group and the audiences to get the best out of them.)

Suggested approach for the leader director

Here are some things which I personally have found useful over the years, when preparing workshops and rehearsals:

Offer your work to God

Find a quiet place, pray about the task ahead, offering yourself and the group up to God. If there are specific problems or need within the group, pray for these, and ask for guidance and help in your dealings with those with whom you will be working. Focus on Christ, and dedicate your work to his glory and ask him to supply your needs as you work in his name. Ask for a blessing on all that you do.

Brainstorm

Focus on the theme of the sketch you are about to work on. Read the passage carefully and jot down notes about its message and the issues which it raises. Don't worry if it doesn't fall into place at once – it will come!

Take another sheet of paper and place the main theme of the sketch you are about to tackle, in the centre of it. Write down around it any ideas and teaching points which come to you regardless of how silly or unconnected they may seem.

Prayer and fellowship

Always begin any session, whether it be discussion, workshop, rehearsal or presentation, with a prayer time for the whole group. I have found the following outline useful in preparation for this time:

1 *Begin with a time of praise.*
 Choose one or two choruses which are closely related to the theme you will be following.

2 *Take time to pray together.*
 Leader's prayer to open the session. Depending on the group offer an open prayer time, or ask others to come prepared to pray on a particular topic. Open prayer will probably take some time to come with a new group and may have to be encouraged in a variety of ways.

3 *Study the text.*
 This can be done at a separate time, as a normal bible study fellowship, or it can be introduced right at the beginning as integral to the Drama Fellowship. I found it useful for the group to meet at my house once every so often, to focus on the issues and ideas within the sketch upon which we were working. It was usually beneficial and had added value, in that it drew the group closer together socially, emotionally and spiritually. Problems were shared and the group learned to build each other up in life as well as in worship.

4 *Dedication.*

Always dedicate the session to the Glory of God.

The role of the director

Read the script

Don't come to it in a fluster as the group begins to gather. Take time to think about it and to read through the tips.

Make personal notes on:

- characters
- themes
- specific issues raised within the sketch
- the main focus
- dramatic high points
- possible staging problems
- issues which might raise difficult questions
- think about the visual effect which needs to be created.

What kind of director?

Authoritarian

Having fixed ideas about the interpretation, character development, and the overall impression of the piece and imposing it on the group. This kind of approach works well with inexperienced and younger groups, enabling them to learn skills of presentation within a firmly disciplined framework.

Democratic

Having some general idea of the overall view, but a more democratic approach, allowing for the imaginative input by members of the group. This kind of director listens to the actors and works out ideas along with them as he goes along, and often uses improvisation, games and drama skills work to lead into the script. He is prepared to change ideas according to need, whilst at the same time holding an overall idea of the message which is to be communicated. This is an essential approach for those devising their own scripts, and works with groups who have some experience.

Experimental

Tends to leave the script aside, throw the ideas open to experimentation and is prepared to let the group try things out even if they do not always work. This is for the confident, experienced older groups with many drama skills upon which they can draw. Use with care!

Combination

Ideally, elements of all these styles are useful when rehearsing. The democratic approach has worked well for me when working with young people, as they feel much more a part of the whole group and like to take some responsibility. The director however, always has the final word when there is a conflict of ideas.

Some advice

In any group there must be some democracy, but:

- The director/leader must have the final word. He can see the overall view, dramatically and personally, which members of the cast often cannot.
- The director must approach all situations with love, tolerance and firmness. Don't get into the habit of throwing your weight around.
- Be honest if you don't know the answers.
- Be prepared to ask for theological or pastoral help if necessary.

Approaching the script

Don't go straight into the script by reading it. Holding bits of paper in the hands deters some young people from showing the full range of their abilities. It is the director's job to develop the full potential of each member of the group to the full. Some people react badly to the script, maybe they don't read very well, or get fixed ideas about what they can and cannot do.

Improvisations based on the script allow everyone in the group to develop many of the characters, broadens their experience and gives them a better idea of the issues and ideas within the theme. The director can gain from new approaches to a particular character, or interpretation of an idea, which can then be incorporated into the final performance.

It is also an ideal means of seeing the potential of individuals in the group. Often I have been surprised at the emergence of hidden talents and also have been made aware of the inhibitions, nervousness, over confidence, concentration and sensitivity of individuals during these sessions. What's more, it helps with the director's nightmare . . . casting!

Tips on characterisation and improvisation can be found in *Rock Solid* which has a series of workshops from which can be drawn ideas for workshops such as this.

Group improvisation
- Work in small groups in given situations or modern parallel themes.
- Give them time to go back to the text upon which the script is based and to improvise their own version.
- Share these with the group as a whole.
- The process of coming to understand the themes and issues of these parables, stories or themes gives the participants a greater understanding of their source material, so that they come to the script with a deeper understanding of its overall meaning.
- Always be prepared to stop and discuss problems and ideas.
- Let them know that they are all part of the growth of the work within the group.

Pick up the script
- Set the text in context. Fill them in on what has happened before, and what happens after. Why was the story, parable, teaching important and how is it important in our Christian life today.
- Always have a theological adviser to keep you all scripturally correct. Invite one to join you to help cover difficult issues.
- Read through the script.
- Cast the sketch and be aware that it is necessary sometimes to cast weaker members in challenging parts, to encourage them, making sure that they are supported by the stronger members of the group.
- Make sure that everyone understands what stage directions are. Where is stage right (**SR**), stage left (**SL**), down stage (**DS**), etc?
- Insist that everyone has a pencil to write in

their moves and any alterations which might be made. This avoids arguments at a later stage!
- Roughly **block out** the moves, taking into account the natural instincts of the cast. (See *Glossary*.)
- Always be aware of the status and tensions between characters at given moments within the text.
- Feel your way through together. Stop and discuss where necessary.
- Refer back to improvisations when appropriate.
- Regularly refer back to the original textual reference.
- Encourage at all times.
- Write down moves in your own script as you go along. This helps to resolve difficulties later on.

The script developed
- Once the moves are **blocked**, run through several times to consolidate and adjust.
- Watch out for **masking** (see *Glossary*.)
- Encourage clear **diction** – all dialogue must be heard by the deaf old lady in the back row! However, discourage shouting!
- Check that the important words are given the right **emphasis**, especially in sketches containing rhythm and rhyme.
- Make sure that they remain **in character** at all times.
- Make the sketch visually interesting by using **levels**. (See *Glossary*.)
- The space you have in which to perform will influence the direction. Always keep this in mind.
- Check that everyone can see all the action. Make a point of watching the sketch from several vantage points.

The how and the why
- Once it is running through reasonably well concentrate on how the action is being performed, develop the style, i.e. melodrama, pantomime, dramatic moments, etc.
- Go with the flow if it works, but be prepared to put down the script and improvise when the feeling is lost, or the focus seems to have become rather blurred.

Halfway house

- There comes a point when no more improvement can be made until lines are learned. The sooner this happens, the better.
- This is the time to stress again that every member of the cast is as important as each other. Scotch any ideas that the one with the most lines has precedence over the one with the least. A piece is as strong as its weakest link. All drama, especially that which is an offering in worship, depends upon teamwork.
- Directors please note that this is the most frustrating time for all and the time when enthusiasm can wane – it's called the pain barrier – but it can be surmounted, with God's help (thankfully!)

Performance

- Pray before you perform and re-dedicate your work to God.
- Allow plenty of time to rehearse in the place where you are to present the sketch, and make adjustments accordingly. Use pews, chairs, blocks, aisles etc. to make sure that everyone can see as well as hear.
- If you are presenting the sketch in a place other than that in which you have rehearsed, (you never know, you may be invited elsewhere!), try to make time to run through and adjust to the new space. Don't go in cold and expect it to work!

Problems, problems

When facing problems or arguments or difficulties which you sense is breaking down relationships or motivation, stop and pray together. This will:

- hand it over to God in whose hands all these thing should be
- calm frayed nerves
- restore peace in equality before God
- heal broken relationships
- keep the director on course and refreshed
- remind everyone why they are there – to worship and proclaim the Lord
- allow individual and personal problems to come into the open, before the Lord, to be shared, so that support can be given
- get all things into perspective – it is only a sketch after all, and is nowhere near as important as unity and Christian love within the group.

Conclusion

Always finish sessions with prayer and allow time to chat and socialise. Drama breaks down barriers, and people are often more open to share their problems or have a need to talk things through with someone. You may have members of your group who are searching for God, they may need to ask questions, or need a sympathetic ear. This is why you are setting out on this crazy venture after all; to worship God, to proclaim his word, and to bring people closer to Christ. Never lose sight of this and you won't go far wrong!

Nehemiah Wimpy and the Wall
Background

CHARACTERS

Narrator   The story teller, but must also be able to change character.

Nehemiah   Confident yet diffident. Able to sustain rapport with the audience.

Artie/Donkey/   Versatile, and able to change character three times. Very physical role.
Israelite

1st Servant   Crucial to the plot. Need to have good facial expression and mime.

2nd Servant   Same as *1st Servant*.

APPROACH

- This sketch relies on pantomime and melodrama for its success.

- The comedy depends greatly upon the sincerity of Nehemiah and the reactions of the other characters. Clarity of diction is vital.

- Reference to **Quick Pics** (see *Glossary*) and some workshop experience would be of great help in the staging.

- All should have some mime practice and experiment with walking on the spot, and building!

- Body language is vital as the sketch relies on various changes of character and mood, particularly from Artie.

- A workshop based on characterisation would be excellent help prior to this sketch being staged.

- The sketch is written in rhyme and has its own rhythm, so some work on emphasis would not go amiss.

- The stage directions are original, but can and indeed should be adapted to the available space.

- The chase and the 'journey' can be taken through the audience if this seems feasible, but it must not slow down the action.

- There are certain elements of 'business' which need careful thought and extra rehearsal. Don't be afraid to experiment.

Nehemiah Wimpy and the Wall
(Nehemiah, chapters 2-4)

Starting Positions

```
USR                                          USL
        X 1st Servant    X 2nd Servant

                 X Narrator



        X Artie                  Nehemiah X
DSR                                          DSL
```

(*All FROZEN with backs to audience*) (**1**)

Narrator   (*CS, turning to audience*) I bring you a tale which should inspire (**2**) Of the building contractor – Nehemiah.

Nehemiah   (*DSL. Nehemiah turns. To audience*) Nehemiah Wimpy, for all alterations, extensions, new building. (*Looks up to heaven*) Guaranteed by the highest authority. (*FREEZE*) (**3**)

Narrator   Artie Xerxes; Emperor. (**4**)

(*Artie turns and gives royal wave to audience*) (**5**)

Narrator   (*To audience apprehensively*) Wait, while I grovel on the floor! (*He moves DSR, kneels and bows to Artie*) There is a man named Nehemiah who dearly wants to see you, sire. (**6**)

Artie   Bring him here right now I say! I'm granting audiences today! (**7**)

(*Narrator rises, bows, moves DSC, beckons Nehemiah, gestures him towards Artie*)

Director's tips

(**1**)   Standing still and relaxed in NEUTRAL (see *Glossary*), feet slightly apart, to give good balance. When in neutral there should be a stillness, and a sense of just being there without making any statement to distract from the forthcoming action.

(**2**)   Don't turn half-heartedly, but with a definite movement. Address whole audience cheerfully and clearly. When indicating Nehemiah don't give a weak 'wet fish' hand movement, but make it a definite gesture. Freeze in position during Nehemiah's next speech.

(**3**)   A flat cap is a useful personal 'prop' for Nehemiah to indicate the character. A broad accent may also help here. He is a stereotypical 'builder'. (For more information about stereotypes and characterisation see *Rock Solid,* pp 34 and 35.) The 'look to heaven' must be reverent, and the tone of voice must echo this. Nehemiah is very earnest and sincere, and his faith is strong, and must be established at once for the rest of the sketch to have credibility.

(**4**)   See (**2**)

(**5**)   Artie must establish his character as arrogant and regal from the outset. Others are addressed as if they are the lowest of the low.

(**6**)   A definite sense of urgency required as he runs to kneel at the feet of Artie. Cast a look at Nehemiah as his name is mentioned. Speak as if in danger of instant execution!

(**7**)   Artie should not look at Narrator as he speaks and waves him in the direction of Nehemiah dismissively.

(Nehemiah moves to Artie, crossing in front of Narrator) (**8**)

(Narrator moves DSL and watches) (**9**)

Artie
(Imperious and offended that Nehemiah is not kneeling)
I'm Artie Xerxes; Emperor.
(Angrily pointing down) What do you think the floor is
for? *(Bellowing fiercely)* GROVEL!

Nehemiah
(Hurriedly kneeling and bowing to the floor) (**10**)
Mr Xerxes, help me please,
as here I grovel, on my knees,
asking Lord, for your permission
to embark upon a mission.
Jerusalem, my Father's city
lies destroyed. Oh Sir, have pity!
Its walls have burned down to the ground
and Lord knows, I must look around.
(Aside, to audience) (**11**)
That God has called me, I'll not tell.
It would not go down very well!
(He assumes prayer position) (**12**)

Artie
Just a moment! *(Moving behind Nehemiah. Accusingly)*
Are you praying? *(Moves DSCL between Nehemiah and
Narrator. Aside to audience)* What in heaven can he be
saying? (**13**)

Nehemiah
(Direct to audience) God has told me what to do. (**14**)
(To Artie, pleading) I think that I should go, don't you?
To my homeland let me ride.
(Aside to audience) In God's will I must abide.

Artie
(Pacing up and down melodramatically) (**15**)
To himself he seems to mutter!
(To Narrator and audience) Methinks this man's a raving
nutter!
(Move DSR. Laughing mockingly) Rebuild Jerusalem on
his own?
He'll never lift one stone alone!
(To audience) Methinks I'll grant this fool's request;
'twill be amusing, quite a jest!

(8)   Nervously. This can be shown by shifting from foot to foot and wringing cap in hands. He has a lucrative and secure position in the court, and in identifying with the nation Israel, is putting himself on the line!

(9)   Move calmly to new position to watch the action. Don't distract from the focus which should be on Artie and Nehemiah.

(10)   Nehemiah should not speak directly to Artie, but occasionally glance in his direction. Speak out to audience, including them as part of the action, hopefully they will empathise with him. He must be sincere and positive, yet with an element of nervousness. It was a big thing for him to do, and important for the Israelites that the walls of Jerusalem were restored. Although Nehemiah was a favourite of the King; a cup bearer, he knew that kings were fickle, and to ask him to reverse the decree that Jerusalem should not be restored, was a dangerous thing to do. Also Artaxerxes did not allow anyone to be miserable, so throughout this request, although nervous, Nehemiah tries to assume cheerfulness. Diffidence and confidence may also be marks of the man of God!

(11)   Use left hand flat, palm facing Artie, to right hand side of mouth in melodramatic 'aside' to audience. Artie must not be aware of this communication, and stares ahead.

(12)   Put on head covering (cap) and hands together in prayer, or raise hands up, whichever feels most comfortable. Remain still.

(13)   Moves behind him, as if listening in, but in a puzzled way, as if he thinks, 'Nehemiah is slightly mad!'

(14)   It must be made abundantly clear to whom Nehemiah speaks. He must gain eye to eye contact with the audience on the 'asides', and show humility to Artie when addressing him. Body language is very important here.

(15)   The pacing must be worked out accurately so that Artie never has his back to the audience when speaking.

	This madman can't do any harm. He'll end up on a funny farm! (*To Nehemiah*) Nehemiah. Go you may, with my blessing on your way! (*Turns with back to audience*) (**16**)
Nehemiah	(*Stands and moves CS with great relief and holds his hands to heaven*) Lord, my God. What now I ask? Make me equal to the task. (**17**)
	(*Nehemiah claps hands*)
Nehemiah	Servants!
	(*Servants turn, move CSR and CSL, kneel before Nehemiah, one on either side*) (**18**)
Nehemiah	You must come with me. (*Exuberantly*) Jerusalem we'll go and see!
	(*Servants/Narrator. Shocked reaction*) (**19**)
Nehemiah	I know it's been destroyed by fire.
	(*Servants/Narrator. Relax*)
Narrator	But . . . (*Thinks*) (**20**)
Servants	(*To audience knowingly*) Leave it all to Nehemiah! (**21**)
	(*Nehemiah leads as they walk as if on a journey. As they walk, they become tired and weary*) (**22**)
Nehemiah	(*Sitting exhausted, CS*) Oh, goodness. I can walk no more (**23**) My legs are stiff, my feet are sore. My head it burneth like a fire. (*Puts head in hands*)
1st Servant	(*To audience over Nehemiah's head*) He's sick and tired! (**24**)
2nd Servant	(*Exaggeratedly sympathetic*) Poor Nehemiah.

(**16**)   Nehemiah's reaction to 'Go you may' must be seen in his facial expression. An extra 'grovel' here would seem quite natural before standing exuberantly. Wait until Artie has assumed NEUTRAL before speaking.

(**17**)   Nehemiah relies on God every step of the way, and although he must show elation here, the seriousness of the situation must be seen to be positively handed over to God. Would that we all could have such trust!

(**18**)   The servants have to remain still for quite a long period. If you wish, they can enter at this point from SR and SL. Make sure that they kneel slightly diagonally, so that the audience can see their expressions.

(**19**)   Moving in unison into a mirror image shock horror pose is effective here. FREEZE it until Nehemiah's reassuring tone in the next speech.

(**20**)   Nehemiah assumes 'Hand to head' thinking position.

(**21**)   Knowing tone of voice, and conspiratorial attitude directed straight to the audience.

(**22**)   They can walk in a circle around the area, twice, becoming gradually more weary until finally Nehemiah sits exhausted. The servants should be carrying bundles (in MIME). Alternatively, they can go up one aisle and down the other if it isn't too far, or they can walk on the spot. It's your choice. The main thing is that the action should hold the audience's interest. Putting down and picking up of bundles, stone in sandal, wiping sweaty brow, etc. Use your imagination. Don't milk it too much, or the audience will have departed for pastures new!

(**23**)   We must really believe in Nehemiah's exhaustion, and much depends on the way he sits, and his facial expression. That old body language again!

(**24**)   Leaning forward, also exhausted, but punching home the lines.

Narrator	(*To audience*) A four-legged friend's his greatest need. I'll find him a worthy steed. (*To Artie*) Oi, you! Donkey! Here boy! (**25**)
Artie	(*Becomes donkey and turns to look at Narrator*) (**26**) Eeaw! (*Narrator holds out carrot to donkey*)
Donkey	(*Trots to Narrator*) Eeeeee – aaaaaw. (*Takes carrot and gallops around*) (**27**)
Nehemiah	(*Trying to catch the donkey*) Whoa boy! Whoa! (*From USC. Very firmly*) (**27**) When I say Whoa, I mean whoa! (**27**)
Servants	(*Bumping business*) When he says 'Whoa' he means 'Whoa'! (**27**)

Stage Positions

```
┌─────────────────────────────────────────────────────┐
│ USR                                             USL   │
│              Nehemiah X X X     X Narrator            │
│                1st servant   2nd servant              │
│                                                       │
│                                                       │
│                                                       │
│                                                       │
│                                                       │
│ DSR      X Donkey                               DSL   │
└─────────────────────────────────────────────────────┘
```

	(*Donkey stops in his tracks DSR*) (**27**) (*Nehemiah takes a running jump onto the donkey's back*) (**28**)
1st Servant	(*Runs DSR. Leads donkey in a circle*) Come on, boy. (**29**) (*2nd Servant follows behind donkey carrying heavy bundles*)

(25) Narrator looks in several directions before 'seeing' Artie. Again, don't take too long.

(26) The donkey is always on its hind legs (stage licence!), but must still assume donkey characteristics and movement. Watch a donkey, see how it moves, how it moves its mouth, what its teeth are like, how it holds its head, etc, and try to physicalise the animal. A direct contrast to Artie's regal bearing.

(27) Donkey gallops USL followed by Nehemiah, 1st servant, 2nd Servant and Narrator, then round in a circle, finally finishing DSR. The other characters finish in a line USC and when Nehemiah says the last 'Whoa', he stops suddenly USC. The others bump into him, in the old pantomime style and fall over each other. They deliver their 'Whoa' line from various positions of disarray. This will need a great deal of practice to get the timing right. If you wish you can chase them through the audience first, again use pantomime style!

(28) Nehemiah can again resort to pantomime, and make a great deal of preparing to mount the donkey, assisted by servants, giving him a drink, fanning him with an imaginary towel, putting him under starters orders, lowering the flag, etc. Again, use all these elements in moderation, work out what is right for you, and don't milk it too much, especially in performance, as you will kill the laughs. A little or nothing is better than overdoing it!

(29) Move from DSR to DSL, in a circle US and finish diagonally as in diagram in script. Mime walk. Left foot on ball of foot, then down on heel, right foot on ball of foot, then down on heel. Use arms and movement of shoulders to give the illusion of walking. Needs much rehearsal. Decide exactly how many steps you are going to take, and whether you are tired or lively at this moment. All halt at the same time.

(Narrator brings up the rear)

(All finish in diagonal from USR to DSL facing audience and move in mime on the spot as if on a journey)

Stage Positions

```
USR                                              USL

                              X Narrator
               X 2nd Servant

      Nehemiah X
            X Artie

      X 1st Servant
DSR                                              DSL
```

Nehemiah	*(Shading eyes)* Our destination lies ahead bathed in sunset, burning red. *(Horrified, climbing off donkey's back to DSCR)* *(Donkey turns with back to audience)* (**30**)
Nehemiah	'Tis Jerusalem's fair wall! (**31**)
1st Servant	*(DSR. To audience. Dismayed)* There's hardly ought left there at all! (**32**)
Nehemiah	*(Pacing across DSL)* This situation seems quite dire! (**33**)
Servants	*(Melodramatically)* Go . . . assess it, Nehemiah. (**34**) *(They move across from DSR to DSL through the 'rubble')*
Nehemiah	Can't get through. There's too much rubble!
Donkey	*(Exasperated)* I give up. Eeee – aaaaw! It's too much trouble!
Nehemiah	Then you're in trouble! *(Beats donkey who runs away USC)*

(30)   Donkey should be totally disinterested, possibly pawing the ground.

(31)   Almost in tears as he views the desolation.

(32)   All survey the scene with the same emotion as Nehemiah.

(33)   Turn and watch Nehemiah as he moves.

(34)   Positively and exaggeratedly, almost commandingly. Nehemiah draws himself to full height, and determined, marches to donkey and leads him through imaginary rubble. The others follow.

(*Donkey turns with back to audience*)

Nehemiah   We'll walk round where e'er we can
and pray, till God reveals his plan.

(*All pray in TABLEAU. Artie becomes an Israelite and joins in*) (**35**)

Nehemiah   (*Gets an idea. Enthusiastically*) We must go rebuild the wall. (**36**)
Build it strong, so it won't fall.

(*Servants, Israelite, Narrator, mime building the wall. Nehemiah moves CSR*) (**37**)

Stage Positions

USR				USL
	X Narrator			
		X Israelite		
X Nehemiah				
			X 1st Servant	
				X 2nd Servant
DSR				DSL

Nehemiah   (*CSR As if foreman of a building site. Bossily*)
Build it up and build it higher.

Servants   (*Together, exhausted and brow beaten. To audience*)
Build it up, says Nehemiah. (*They sit wearily*) (**37**)

Narrator   (*Together. Moaning as they sit exhausted DSR*) Can't build a city on our own!

Nehemiah   We Will build it . . . stone by stone! (*Moving to them, exhorting them to work*)

(*Servants sit DSL, Israelite, Narrator, wearily shake their heads*)

(35) Make a QUICK PIC (See *Glossary*) of prayer CS using interesting positions and LEVELS. (See *Rock Solid,* pp 14 and 62.)

(36) If everyone is physically deflated the change of mood when Nehemiah gets his idea, it will have more impact. Swift change of facial expressions will also get over the new enthusiasm.

(37) With great exertion, wall stretches from USR to DSL. All move with determination to new positions, and begin building. Think of different activities, measuring, carrying stones, cementing, etc. Make sure that the wall 'grows'. Gradually become more and more disillusioned, again body language is important!

Nehemiah	(*Moving CS. Commandingly*) Rise and build, O Israelites. (**38**)
	(*Servants, reluctantly stand*)
	Rise and build! And get it right!
	(*Israelite/Narrator, reluctantly stand and look at Nehemiah*)
	A blueprint God has made for man. Build, according to His plan!
	(*Nehemiah enthusiastically slaps one of them on the back, before joining in with the 'building at the down stage end of it. To audience*) With God's help, we'll never tire. (*Continues to build*) (**39**)
Servants	(*To audience as if to inspire them*) Rise up! And build . . . (**40**)
All	(*To audience*) Like Nehemiah!(**41**)
	(*Freeze in TABLEAU*)
	(*Nehemiah turns, and slowly raises his hands to heaven, finally finishing in Freeze Frame*) (**42**)

(38)   Hands raised.

(39)   Nehemiah moves to Narrator and Israelite, then to Servants, using hands outstretched in 'pleading motion'. Servants, Israelite and Narrator look at each other, then at Nehemiah, then up to heaven. Smiles of realisation cross their faces. Energetically, they go back to the 'wall' and begin to build.

(40)   Turn to audience and address them directly.

(41)   All gesture with left hand to Nehemiah, who continues to build.

(42)   It is important that Nehemiah's move is focused, as he gives the glory to God. Hold the TABLEAU for three to five seconds. Servants, narrator and Israelite make the TABLEAU interesting by using different LEVELS when gesturing to Nehemiah.

Daniel in the Den
Background

CHARACTERS

Daniel   Serious but sympathetic.

Darius   Imposing and proud. Able to be commanding.

3 Governors/   Three people needed who can change character effectively from governor to
3 Lions   lion. Good mime and movement required, and patience to work at it!

Narrator   Clear speaking voice, an ability to empathise with the audience and get
                       involved in the watching as well as the telling of the story.

APPROACH

- This sketch must be very slick, with a fair amount of pace.

- The comedy depends greatly upon the seriousness of Daniel, and the exaggerated evil of the governors.

- It is useful to create a workshop based on the story before attempting the script. (See *Introduction* for ideas.)

- QUICK PICS are an established part of the sketch, also the use of LEVELS. Characterisation is vital, as all but Daniel and the Narrator should be played in caricature in a stylised way.

- The Narrator must establish a rapport with the audience.

- Some experiment with the change from Governors to Lions, and from lions to 'pussy Cats' is important. The two roles *must* be different. Get your cast to observe cats and lions if possible, and to develop distinctive animal movements.

- Clarity of diction is vital.

- The sketch is written mainly in verse and has its own rhythm. The words to be emphasised are in darker print to help the less experienced and younger members of the group.

- The stage directions are as the original, but this does not mean that they are written in tablets of stone! They can and should be adapted to the space in which you are working. Don't be afraid to experiment and use the ideas of the cast.

- Have fun!

Daniel in the Den
(Daniel, chapter 6)

(Each character is frozen in position as indicated below.) (**1**)

Starting Positions

USR		**USL**
	Darius **X**	
1st Governor **X**	**X** 2nd Governor	
	X 3rd Governor	
X Narrator		Daniel **X**
DSR		**DSL**

Narrator	*(DSR facing audience)* **Ma**ny **gov**ernors had **Dar**ius the **king** He ex**pect**ed **them** to do **ev**erything. *(1st Governor mimes fanning Darius)* (**2**) *(2nd Governor mimes taking notes at Darius' dictation)* (**2**) *(3rd Governor kneels and bows several times)* (**2**)
Narrator	*(Looking conspiratorially DSL towards Daniel)* **One** of these **gov**ernors (**3**)
Daniel	*(Politely interrupting, with a glance at the Narrator, before addressing the audience)* Whose **name** was **Dan**! (**4**)
Narrator	*(Acknowledging Daniel with a nod of the head)* Thank you! Was an **Is**raelite, **hon**est,
Daniel	*(Stands proudly to full height)* (**5**) A **very wise man**!

Director's tips

(**1**)　　It is useful in terms of the audience, and because of his position as King, if he can be raised up on a block or a step. The use of LEVELS is important when staging sketches, as the visual impact is as important as the verbal.

(**2**)　　Each of the moves are done simultaneously. Darius must appear to be giving orders. Think carefully about the mime, and be sure that it is accurate. There are *no* props, but the audience must believe in the activities. Make sure that Darius is not MASKED.

(**3**)　　Daniel and the Narrator must appear to be working together to tell the story. The Narrator can help here by carefully watching the story and inter acting with Daniel where possible.

(**4**)　　A glance at each other here, as Daniel continues the sentence. Governors and Darius continue to mime in the background, but taking care not to upstage the Narrator by over enthusiastic movement.

(**5**)　　Daniel takes a breath and must be seen visibly to grow taller in stature. He must be proud, but not arrogant. Facial expression is important here, a slight smile may help. Better still, get the actor to think about a situation which makes him feel good, and transfer that feeling to the character of Daniel.

(Daniel puts hands together in prayer and looks heavenwards for inspiration!) (**6**)

Narrator	**Da**rius the **king** Thought **Dan**iel was **BRILL**.
Darius	Brill! *(Waves dismissively to Governors and gestures towards Daniel)* (**7**)
	(Governors irritated, move to congregate in a group CSL with jealous glances at Daniel) (**8**)
Darius	I ad**mire** his int**eg**rity **And** his **skill**.
Narrator	**Da**rius said to **Dan**
Darius	**O'er** my **king**dom you shall **rule**
	(Daniel moves USC and kneels before Darius with back to audience)
Darius	*(To audience)* I **like** a clever man *(To Daniel)* and you **ain't** no **fool**!
	(Daniel and Darius freeze during next dialogue) (**9**)
1st Governor	*(Moving DSL)* **We** other **govern**ors were **filled with hate**.
2nd Governor	*(Moving, just behind and to the right of 1st Governor and leaning round him to the right)* (**10**) We were **jeal**ous,
3rd Governor	*(Moving to right of 1st Governor, and slightly behind to the left)* (**10**) We were **mad**,
1st Governor	We were **most IRATE**.
	(Governors all change posture and make quick pic of anger) (**11**)
Narrator	*(Shrugging shoulders and addressing audience directly)* Actually, they were very narked off with the whole situation! (**12**)

(**6**)   He must not look comically 'pious' at this stage, but serious and strong.

(**7**)   Darius must be imperious, dictatorial and very much in charge. The reaction of each governors must be of a low status person reacting to a high status one. The dismissive wave works well with the right hand, palm down, arm raised, as a kind of double flick movement, with wrist action. Then the gesture to Daniel can be strong and approving in contrast, with the left arm stretched towards him, palm upwards.

(**8**)   It is vital that the Governors are established immediately as the 'baddies'. Much reliance here on facial expression and body language. Mean looks and twisted stance are the order of the day! (And don't forget the occasional sinister laugh!)

(**9**)   It is vital to be totally still during a FREEZE, otherwise attention will be drawn away from the focus of the section which is the reaction of the Governors.

(**10**)   1st Governor – on 'hate', FREEZE in appropriate pose, with a twisted expression.
2nd Governor – use the stress on the word 'jealous' to FREEZE in a twisted jealous shape, with mean expression.
3rd Governor – on 'mad' FREEZE raised hands in wild gesture.

(**11**)   All Governors – on the second syllable of 'irate', change posture and expression to make a QUICK PIC (See *Glossary/Rock Solid*) of anger. Make sure that you use different LEVELS (See *Glossary/Rock Solid*) and shapes.

(**12**)   This line must be delivered 'tongue in cheek', with the assumption that the Narrator knows that the audience realise he is stating the obvious. The comedy comes from the extreme expressions of the Governors.

(Daniel rises and moves to R of Darius, takes notes, mimes discussion of important issues during next dialogue)

1st Governor   *(Determined)* We **must** find **some**thing **wrong** with **Dan**! **(13)**

2nd Governor   *(At a loss)* He **can't** be **such** a **perf**ect **man**?

3rd Governor   *(Excited that he has found a fault)* Does he pick his nose?

Governors   *(Shaking heads disappointedly)* No!

1st Governor   *(Raising finger with enthusiastic expression)* Does he ever forget to kneel when the king enters?

Governors   *(Sagging physically)* No!

2nd Governor   *(Frowning)* Do his feet smell when he takes off his shoes?

Governors   *(Exasperated)* No!

3rd Governor   *(Angrily)* He's **Dari**us's **pet**, is **a**rrogant **Dan**!

1st Governor   We **must** get **rid** of him **if** we **can**!

(Governors go into a huddle)

Narrator   They **planned** and **plot**ted,

Governors   *(Still in a huddle, but with gesticulation and mimed mutterings)* **(14)** **Plot**ted and **plan**ned.

Narrator   **Tried** to find a **way** to get **Dan**iel **BANNED**.

(Daniel during next dialogue moves DSR to Narrator as if on Darius' business. They FREEZE in discussion pose)

(Darius folds arms and adopts 'kingly' posture and freezes as Daniel moves)

1st Governor   *(Turn to audience)* Daniel is **God** fearing – a re**lig**ious **man**.

(13)   The following dialogue must have pace and attack, and the governor's must be carica-
         tured. Keep the rhythm going where indicated, but make the most of the ideas! This can
         definitely be 'played to the gallery'!

(14)   As they are still in a conspiratorial huddle, they must show their mood by their backs and
         their arm gesticulations. They must do at least two. Occasionally they can glance outwards
         as if checking that they are not overheard.

2nd Governor	(*Turn to audience and kneel in mocking prayer*) He **al**ways prays to **Him** up **there** when**ev**er he **can**. (*FREEZE*) (**15**)
3rd Governor	(*To audience. Raising hands in exasperation*) **Dar**ius ex**pects** us to **wor**ship him as **king**. (*FREEZE*) (**15**)
Governors	But **Dan**iel won't stop **pray**ing for **any**thing! (*Look at each other in desperation*)
1st Governor	(*Slight pause*) **If** there was a **law** for**bid**ding **pray**er Dan is **bound** to break the **rule**
3rd Governor	(*Gleefully grinning, jumping and clapping hands*) And we'll **have** him **right there**!
2nd Governor	(*Smugly nodding*) By the short and curlies!
Governors	Yeah! (*All make hand gesture of unity. Then swiftly, led by 1st Governor, move in a diagonal line USCL of Darius.*) (**16**)
	(*Daniel moves CS, kneels in prayer*)
	(*1st Governor whispers into Darius' ear*)
Narrator	(*As 1st Governor whispers*) They **went** to the **King** and **whis**pered in his **ear**. (*To audience, horrified*) (**17**)
Darius	(*Standing with horrified expression*) **All** should worship **me** . . . (**18**)
	(*Governors step back in fear, visibly shaking*) (**19**)
Darius	(*Shouting at Governors angrily*) Is **that** quite **clear**?
Governors	(*Looking with smug expressions at the praying Daniel*) Yes, **SIR**!
	(*1st Governor moves DS to Daniel, taps him on the shoulder, then returns to R of Darius USCR*) (**20**)

(15)   Exaggerated movement before the freeze.

(16)   The hand gesture which worked for our group is as follows, but feel free to work out your own!
1st Governor puts hand out palm upwards (first beat).
2nd Governor places his right hand, palm down on top of it (second beat).
3rd Governor places his left hand on top, palm down (third beat).
Try the moves first and then 'Yeah!' Experiment with the 'Yeah' first and the moves afterwards and see which one works best for your group. The main thing to remember is that it mustn't be laboured, but slick and well timed!

(17)   Taking the audience into his confidence and assuming that they feel the horror he feels.

(18)   Make this a big and impressive move. Darius must be every inch the tyrannical dictator. The reaction of the governors will stress that all are afraid of him.

(19)   All governors step back on right foot at exactly the same time with exactly the same expression as they freeze. It is really important to rehearse these little bits and to get them flowing smoothly, as it makes all the difference to the impact of the script.

(20)   There must be a triumphant expression and walk here, and the tap on the shoulder should be bossy and peremptory.

(Daniel stands and moves back SR to narrator)

Narrator   *(To audience, but including Daniel who listens intently, shaking head)* And **so** he de**creed** that **no** one could **pray**.

Narrator   Un**less** they prayed to **him**!

Darius   **This** law **stands** for **thir**ty **days**! *(Moving CSR towards Daniel as he speaks)* **(21)**
If this law is **brok**en by **any fool**ish **men**
Then **I** will redi**rect** them to the **lion**'s **den**! *(Moves USC to his 'throne')*

1st Governor   *(Step forward to audience with thumbs up sign)* Jolly good! **(22)**

2nd Governor   *(Wagging finger as he steps forward)* Quite right!

3rd Governor   *(Folding arms, smugly)* Just so!

(Governors return to positions they were in at start of sketch and freeze) **(23)**

(Daniel moves in a semicircle USC to DSL where he mimes the actions described by the narrator) **(24)**

Narrator   **Dan**iel went **home**, disre**gard**ed the **law**
Got out his **pray**er mat, and **knelt** on the **floor**.
He con**tin**ued to **pray (25)**

Governors   *(Turn to audience gleefully)* **three** times a **day**! *(Turn and whisper to Darius)* **(26)**

Narrator   And **joy**fully the **gov**ernors gave **Daniel away**.

Darius   *(Shock. Horror)* He isn't! **(27)**

1st Governor   *(Smugly towards audience)* He is.

Darius   *(In disbelief to 2nd Governor)* Not Daniel?

2nd Governor   *(Self-satisfied, to audience)* He certainly is!

(**21**) Pointing imperiously towards Daniel, and then moving hand across body to include audience.

(**22**) 1st and 2nd Governors hold their positions until 'just so' plus one second after. 3rd Governor hold position for one second after 'just so'.

(**23**) All move together in unison back to frozen start positions. Scurry in servile manner.

(**24**) Daniel's demeanour must be in direct contrast to that of the Governors. Upright and honest, proud but not arrogant, although somewhat determined and defiant.

(**25**) Complete the following as individual actions, taking care over each one. Not too slow though or it will descend into comedy! And Daniel is the straight man in this sketch! Roll out mat. Kneel. Hands in prayer. Look up. Close eyes. Head bowed in prayer.

(**26**) Swift turn to audience to deliver line, and swift turn back. Say it with feeling, these guys have just gained their heart's desire . . . to 'get' Daniel.

(**27**) Turn heads only to audience, again exactly together, and then look at Darius, exactly together.

3rd Governor	(*Triumphantly to audience*) And he says he won't stop . . . (*To Darius*) not for anyone! (**28**)
	(*Governors take a step towards audience and walk once in a circle on the spot, rubbing hands during the next two or three lines*)
Darius	(*Stands*) **Nas**ty, **nas**ty. . .**ve**ry **ve**ry **nas**ty!(**29**) (*Shouting*) **Dan**iel! Stop **pray**ing You've **brok**en my **law** (*Moves CS*) How **dare** you **Dan**iel What **are** you praying **for**? I'll give you a re**prieve** If your **pray**er you will **leave**.
Governors	(*To audience in complete disbelief*) He'll give **him** a re**prieve**? **This** we can't be**lieve**!
Daniel	(*Still praying*) I **pray** to my **God** (**30**) The **Lord most high**
Daniel	**He** rules **over** all **earth** and **sky**.
Darius	(*Infuriated*) What about me? Worship me! (*Tantrum*) (**31**)
Governors	(*Moving around Darius and gesturing towards him*) Worship him. (**32**)
Daniel	(*Firmly*) No. (**33**)
Darius	(*Angrily*) Yes!
Daniel	(*Patient but firm*) No.
Darius	(*Shouting*) Yes!
Governors	(*Turn and move towards Daniel*) NO?
1st Governor	**Naughty naughty** . . . **ve**ry **ve**ry **naughty**! (**34**)
Darius	**Throw** him to the lions.

(28)   To audience as before, and then gesture towards Darius.

(29)   Darius must come across here as a tyrannical dictator. Definitely the demon king!

(30)   As Daniel speaks, Look up. Open eyes. Look at audience. Patience is the name of his game.

(31)   Have a really childish tantrum here, for no longer than three seconds, and suddenly stop.

(32)   Freeze once in position around Darius.

(33)   Daniel must appear very patient here and let Darius build up the anger and frustration to fever pitch. Governors show their enjoyment of the situation with evil smiles.

(34)   Wag finger at Daniel as if to a naughty infant. All gather around him. Don't mask!

Governors	(*Turn and bow to Darius, rubbing hands in glee*) With **pleas**ure, sir.
	(*1st Governor throws Daniel CS*)
	(*Darius move USC and stand in front of 'throne'*)
	(*Governors change character into Lions as they speak*) (**35**)
Lions	(*To Daniel fiercely*) **Grow**ly, **grow**ly . . . very very **grow**ly!
1st Lion	(*Move to R of Daniel*) **Mun**chy, **mun**chy. He looks **crun**chy! (**36**)
	(*Daniel kneels up*)
2nd Lion	(*Moves behind Daniel, leaning over him*) **Slur**py, **slur**py. **Go**ing to have a **burpy**!
3rd Lion	(*Lies down in front of Daniel*) **Creep**y **peep**y, **meals** make me so **sleep**y!(**37**)
Daniel	So they've thrown me in with the lions.
Lions	GRRRRRRRRRRRRR! (**38**)
Narrator	However, Daniel still trusted in God. So he prayed . . .
	(*Daniel adopts prayer position as before*)
Narrator	(*Leaning confidentially to audience*) Now **ev**en though the **li**ons were **very** very **fierce**.
Lions	(*Repeat fierce movements*) GRRRRRRRRR!
Narrator	**God** protected **Dan**iel So . . . the **li**ons became . . . **quite nice**.
Lions	(*All become gentle pussy cats during the growl*) Grrrrrrrrr . . . Miaow! (**39**)
	(*Darius moves DSR and looks on in amazement*)

DANIEL IN THE DEN

(35)   This is a difficult bit! The governors must change into King of beasts a la 'Lion King'. It is a good idea for the actors to watch such animals, and to experiment with movement and slow changing from one mood to another. Remember the claws and the toss of the mane, etc.

(36)   As governor moves to Daniel's right, make sure that he goes behind him, to get into position.

(37)   Keep up the lion character here. Although they may lick lips, and scratch ears, they must be fierce! Otherwise the next change won't have impact. Experiment again and pool ideas.

(38)   The growl must be pantomime scary. 1st and 2nd lions growl into Daniel's ears. He can look scared at this point. (Well wouldn't you be scared if faced by three hungry lions?) 3rd lion lies on floor in front of Daniel with claws raised as if to strike.

(39)   This is it! The change from lion to soft pussycat! Silly smiles and exaggerated friendly cat movements will help here. 1st lion stroke Daniel with paw. 2nd lion rub against his shoulder. 3rd lion roll over with paws in the air. A purr could help the illusion . . . as long as it is quiet enough for the rest of the scene to be heard!

Narrator	(*To Darius*) **This** goes to **prove** that . . . if you **pray** every **day** Wher**ev**er you **are** You'll keep the **li**ons at **bay**
Darius	(*Taking Daniel SR*) You're **safe** and un**harmed** Your **God** is a **won**der To **save** you this **way.** (*Examining him, amazed*) You're **not** torn a**sun**der. From **this** very **day** **Pray**ers shall be made To **Dan**iel's **God** (*Kneels*) **His** name be **praised**!
All (*To audience*)	**Pray**er every **day** Helps you **work** rest and **play** (*Moving around Daniel and Darius*) **Pray**er every **day** Keeps the **li**ons a**way**!
Lions	(*Repeat pussy cat moves*) Miaow. (**40**)

(*Narrator moves DSC. Gives thumbs up to audience*)

(*All FREEZE*) (**41**)

Final Positions

USR		**Block**		USL
			1st Lion **X**	**X** 2nd Lion
	Narrator **X**		Daniel **X**	**X** Darius
				X 3rd Lion
DSR				DSL

(**40**)   3rd lion rolls towards audience. All make the miaow long drawn out.

(**41**)   Hold the freeze for three seconds before relaxing into neutral and exiting. A tip here, don't relax in bits and bobs . . . do it in unison, it's much more professional.

The Committee
Background

CHARACTERS

Mrs Clarke   A very enthusiastic church worker, who likes to organise others.

Miss Peel   An ex-missionary with an inflated idea of her own importance. Anxious to let people know what good work she has done.

Ms Brown   Miss Peel's co-worker. Has been used to running things without much opposition.

Sally Young   The youth representative on the worship committee. Idealistic and disturbed by the lack of practical unity and consideration in the church. A little in awe of the older members.

APPROACH

- This sketch addresses the personality clashes which can occur within a church community, and which can be very divisive. It is important that the audience are shocked by the behaviour of the committee, and yet recognise those motives which are present in all of us at some time.

- This is also a comment on the place young people are often given within the church setting, so it is important that Sally does not come over as rude, but positive!

- So much of this sketch depends on tone of voice and the inner motivation of the characters, that it would be well worthwhile to develop a history for the characters, and a background as to why they are there. This hopefully will enable the young people to understand some of the motivations and problems of their elders. (Some work on Characterisation will help as part of a workshop leading up to this sketch. See *Rock Solid,* pp 34, 35, 'Stereotypes', 'Personality Profiles', and 'Head-to-Head'.)

- This is one of the few sketches where items of costume and an occasional prop can be used to help make the characters real. A notepad, pencil and paper, a hat for Mrs Clarke, large identical crosses for Miss Peel and Miss Brown, a handbag in which to rummage perhaps?

The Committee
(1 Corinthians 3:5-9)

(All characters are frozen in TABLEAU of committee meeting) (**1**)

Starting Positions

```
USR                                              USL




         X Sally Young      X Miss Peel

      X Mrs Clarke              X Ms Brown

DSR                                              DSL
```

Miss Peel	*(Sits, self-satisfied)* Right. Now you know why we've come here tonight. We've come here for a 'bouncing ideas off each other' session. The theme, as you know, for Sunday Service is 'More than Conquerors for God'. *(Smiling expectantly at everyone)* Should we begin with a song or a prayer? (**2**)
Mrs Clarke	*(Bossily)* Definitely a prayer. That will get everyone into a reverent mood. Then a song by the singing group. (Dismissively) Then we could have the mission input, or whatever you're doing. (**3**)
Ms Brown	*(Crossly)* No! I don't think that's the right order. *(Sally Young frowns)* (**4**)
Miss Peel	I agree ... *(Offended)* We didn't spend eighteen months in China doing mission work, to be considered less important than a group of singers. (**5**)
Ms Brown	And anyway, the singers will completely ruin the atmosphere we want to create for our slide show ... unless they sing in Chinese of course. *(Laughs at her own joke)* (**6**)

Director's tips

(1) The characters can be seated or one can be standing, as if addressing the rest. Seats are useful in this sketch, but not absolutely necessary. Do not use chairs if it means that people at the back can't see faces as this is most frustrating for an audience. Check your SIGHT LINES (See *Glossary*) when setting the chairs. Make the frozen picture interesting to look at. It must communicate 'committee meeting'! I'm sure you'll have ideas about that!

(2) This speech should be delivered very politely with a smile, but also with a firmness, 'iron hand in velvet glove'?

(3) Mrs Clarke should appear uncomfortable from the beginning. She is obviously irritated by the agenda, and wants to impose her will upon the others. Sally Young has her bible in her hand, and looks innocently from one to another as the conversation progresses.

(4) She recognises the conflict and is possibly wondering what is going to happen next.

(5) She exchanges a conspiratorial glance with Miss Peel. Both are determined to have their way, and this must communicate to the audience immediately.

(6) This must be extremely sarcastic, and Miss Peel must share the joke by joining in with polite, but cool laughter.

Sally	(*Politely interrupting*) Couldn't we . . . (**7**)
Mrs Clarke	(*Ignoring Sally*) Music is important in worship, and my singers rehearse every week. Giving up their valuable time. (**8**)
	(*Sally leafing through her Bible while listening, perturbed, to the conversation*)
Miss Peel	(*Decisively*) Open with prayer, a hymn, the mission talk, your singers, another prayer, a hymn and the benediction.
Catherine	(*Extremely put out*) Singing is being pushed into the background, and it's important to praise. (**9**)
Miss Peel	(*Reluctantly*) Well . . . yes. (*Dismissively*) But I suppose your group will just have to take a back seat this time, (*Smugly*) because *we* have a sermon. (*Pause*) . . . with *slides*. (**10**)
Mrs Clarke	(*Angrily*) I object! (**11**)
	(*Sally relieved, smiles confidently as she finds what she is looking for*) (**12**)
Miss Peel	(*Angrily polite, through gritted teeth*) Why don't you choose the first hymn? (**13**)
Sally	(*Polite but hesitant, indicating her bible*) Er, . . . excuse . . . (**14**)
Mrs Clarke	(*Stands. Ignoring her totally, then enthusiastically as if to herself*) Thine Be the Glory?
	(*Sally sits*)
Mrs Clarke	Hymn number 398, gets us off to a good start – and it's my favourite! (*Pauses patronisingly*) In Psalms and Songs. (**15**)
Miss Peel	(*Relieved*) We don't have Psalms and Songs.

(7)   Sally smiles as she tries to make the peace, and is obviously disturbed at the turn the meeting is taking. At this point, after she has been interrupted, she leafs through her bible, obviously looking for a particular reference.

(8)   It is vital that Mrs Clarke pointedly ignores Sally and that she jumps in on cue immediately. It is also useful if Sally thinks of the completion of her suggestion so that it can tail off in surprise at the rudeness of the interruption.

(9)   Tone of voice is important here, as Mrs Clarke takes offence. Also body language, she might sit stiffly on the edge of her chair at this point.

(10)   Make sure that there is a pause before 'with slides' to give it greater emphasis, and to accentuate the icy politeness.

(11)   If chairs are being used, Mrs Clarke could stand at this point, obviously very angry. Ms Peel and Ms Brown share a look of triumph.

(12)   Sally takes a breath and sits on the edge of her chair as if to put her point of view, but is deflated as she is interrupted before she can get a word out. This can be shown by the way she sinks back into her seat.

(13)   This can be made to seem icily polite by slowing the speech slightly and enunciating clearly as if dealing with an annoying unruly child.

(14)   Sally stands, determined to be heard, indicating her Bible clearly. This must be a positive not a half-hearted movement. All eyes should be on her momentarily.

(15)   A self-satisfied smile helps during the pause, also to point the line Mrs Clarke could sit.

Mrs Clarke	(*Smugly leaning forward with a look of triumph*) I've arranged to borrow copies.
Miss Peel	(*Aggressively*) What about testimony? And if so *who's* doing it? (**16**)
Mrs Clarke	(*Self-righteously*) Not me. I do the music, and the music takes a *long* time.
Sally	(*Stands. Very frustrated by now*) Er . . . excuse me!
	(*All look at her*) (**17**)
Ms Brown	(*To Sally*) Do you want to say something?
Sally	(*Determined*) Yes please. It says here. (*Reading from the Bible*) The one who *sows* and the one who *waters* really do not matter. It is *God* who matters, because he makes the plants grow. There is *no difference* between the man who sows and the man who waters. God will reward *each one* according to the work he has done. We are *partners* working together for *God* . . . (*Looking at them all*) and *you* are God's field! (**18**)
	(*All FREEZE with shocked looks. Sally with a questioning look*) (**19**)

(**16**)   It must be obvious here that she expects to be asked to do it!

(**17**)   The look must be extremely irritated, as if she has just crawled out from under a stone, and is considered very unimportant.

(**18**)   To be read with great emphasis, clearly, and with glances at the others. Also some of it must be directed at the audience, for they too are God's field, and we want to make them think about their own ingrained attitudes.

(**19**)   Each character must decide for themselves exactly what their reaction will be, and the TABLEAU at the end must be held for three to five seconds, so that the audience can see what their reaction is, and identify with it. Guilt? Annoyance? Surprise?

Shamus
Background

CHARACTERS

Shamus Smugg   Versatility needed here, and the ability to age from babyhood to old age.

Jesus   Sensitive approach required. A quiet presence. Changes role several times so must also be versatile.

Narrator   Clear and expressive speaking voice.

Chorus A, B, C   All are lively and versatile, with the ability to move with precision.

APPROACH

- This is probably one of the hardest sketches in the book, and needs much research into the needs of the world and the materialistic attitude to life in the Western World. It can have a powerful impact on an audience however, and it is well worth spending time on it.

- It depends on a combination of stereotype and reality, and I would recommend some character-isation work and personality profile work especially on the needy people. It can provide a springboard for investigation into these areas. Indeed, you may discover other areas of need which you could represent, so feel free to change the 'needs' if it feels right to you.

- It is a sketch which needs pace and attack and energy, involving many quick changes of character for the Choruses.

- The audience need to be involved, so they must be addressed directly wherever indicated.

- As with the other sketches, the moves may have to be adapted according to space, but don't let this slow down the pace.

- It would be very worthwhile to pick out a variety of activities from *Rock Solid* or other drama books, and devise workshops along the themes introduced in the sketch, covering the skills required as recommended in the introduction.

Shamus
(Matthew 25:42-46)

Starting Positions (**1**)

```
USR                                                    USL

                        Chorus B
                           X
               Chorus A  X        X Chorus C
                           X
                        Shamus
                        (sitting)
Jesus X
DSR                                                    DSL
```

Chorus A, B, C   (*Turning to audience*) Jesus said . . . (**2**)

Jesus   (*To audience*) I stand at the door and knock. If anyone hears my voice and opens the door, I will enter and eat with him, and he will eat with me. (*Watches action*)

(*Shamus as baby, lies on ground and kicks*) (**3**)

Chorus A   (*Looking admiringly at Shamus and then to audience*) Shamus Smugg. Born April 1st 1998. (**4**)

Chorus B   (*Tickling him*) Isn't he lovely, little Shamus?

(*Shamus gurgles*)

Chorus C   Coochy coochy coo!

Chorus B   Diddums den.

(*Shamus. Raspberry*)

Chorus B   (*Draws back, offended, as Mum to Chorus C*) Takes after you! (**5**)

Chorus C   (*As Dad*) Looks like you!

Director's tips

(1)   All characters are in position with backs to the audience, standing in neutral except Shamus who is sitting. All are in frozen TABLEAU.

(2)   It is important that Jesus includes the whole audience in what he is saying.

(3)   Shamus immediately becomes a baby, gurgling and kicking his legs. Don't overdo the gurgling or the others won't be heard!

(4)   In the character of admiring relatives. Talking as if to a baby, but including the audience. Tone of voice is definitely condescending baby talk, and very exaggerated.

(5)   Facial expressions and reactions to the 'raspberry' must be horrified and larger than life.

Chorus A	(*To audience*) Now he's two. (**6**)
Shamus	(*Sits up*) Me want potty. (**7**)
Chorus B	(*As Dad offering him a potty in mime*) There you are little Shamus. Have a little tinkle. (**8**)
	(*Chorus A, B, C turn backs on Shamus politely, and move away a little*)
Shamus	(*Sitting on 'potty'*) Tinkle tinkle! (*Beams widely*) Mummy! Daddy! Me me me me me me me me me me! (**9**)
Chorus A, B, C	(*Turning to audience*) This is Shamus. Now he's three. (**10**)
Shamus	(*To audience*) Me like motor cars best. (*Gleefully*) Me like smashing em up. (*Careering around*) Brrrrrrm brrrrrrrm brrrrrrrm. (**11**)
Chorus B	(*Moves DSL with Chorus C. Shaking head at his behaviour*) Destroys his toys at one heck of a rate.
	(*Shamus becomes as an eight-year-old*) (**12**)
	(*Chorus A moves SR*) (**13**)
Chorus C	(*To Chorus B conversationally*) He's growing up fast. (**14**)
Shamus	(*To audience*) I'm Shamus . . . I'm eight! I've got a sister . . . Her smelly name's Kate. I *hate* sisters. (*Moves SR to Chorus A. Nips her*) (**15**)
Chorus A	(*As Kate*) Ow! (*Moves DSR to Chorus B and C*) Shamus naughty. Shamus mean! (**16**)
Chorus B and C	(*Moves towards Shamus*) The naughtiest boy we've ever seen. (**17**)
	(*Shamus runs away DSL, pulling out tongue at them*)

(6)   There must be clear distinction between the narration element of the story and the characterisation. A different accent could be used by 'parents' to help this distinction.

(7)   Adopting a spoiled baby voice.

(8)   As dad.

(9)   Squatting as if on potty. Make sure to keep in baby character and maintain voice.

(10) Matter of fact narration directly to audience.

(11) As an out of control toddler thoroughly absorbed in his cars. He can run them up and down Chorus A and B who should show restrained irritation.

(12) It is very important to get the age differences. Try to watch a typical eight-year-old and adopt some of his mannerisms! Most people know a naughty boy they can base the character on.

(13) As a patiently exasperated observer, definitely disapproving.

(14) As proud parent.

(15) Showing off. Let an evil expression cross his face as he moves to attack his sister. Chorus A becomes a little girl as soon as the word 'sister' is heard.

(16) A violent reaction and scream as she is nipped. Then running and crying as if to tell tales to Mum and Dad.

(17) Wagging fingers and speaking crossly. The last part of the line should be shared with the audience in an assumption that they will agree with the statement.

Chorus C	(*To audience*) Doesn't listen, (**18**)
Chorus B	(*To audience*) disobeys.
Chorus A	(*Moving CS to Chorus B and C*) Shamus! Shamus! (**19**)
Chorus A, B, C	(*To Shamus*) Mend your ways! (**20**)
	(*Jesus watches*) (**21**)
Shamus	(*Moves DSC, to audience*) I hate parents, too. They're always nagging. (**22**)
Chorus B	(*Over his right shoulder*) Shamus, don't do this! Shamus, don't do that!
Shamus	Shut up, Mum!
Chorus C	(*Moves L of Shamus*) Don't speak to your mother like that!
Chorus A	(*Moves DSR as 'door'*) (**23**)
	(*Jesus rings bell*)
Chorus A, B, C	Ding dong! (*B and C move CSL in a diagonal line*) (**24**) Shamus, answer the door! And be quick about it!
Shamus	(*Peering through letterbox*) Yes? (**25**)
Jesus	(*Bending to speak through letterbox*) Hello, Shamus. My name's Jesus. The person you've been waiting for.
Shamus	I haven't been waiting for anyone . . . and me mam doesn't want any double glazing. So push off! (*Moves DSC and mimes playing on computer*) (**26**)
Jesus	(*Through letterbox*) I'll call again another day.
Shamus	(*Sarcastically*) You do that.
	(*Jesus watches*)

(**18**) To audience in exasperation. Chorus A joins them.

(**19**) Speaks to Shamus, shaking head, as teacher discovering him doing something really naughty.

(**20**) All turn to Shamus and wag fingers at him as they speak.

(**21**) Jesus must be always present but just watching kindly without extreme reaction. He must never distract from the action when he watches.

(**22**) Shamus becomes a little older here, and tries to enlist the sympathy of the audience. But he speaks rudely and we hope the audience will recognise the situation but laugh unsympathetically.

(**23**) Standing with back to Jesus, and slightly upstage with left hand held parallel with ground at shoulder height. Jesus mimes pressing doorbell on Chorus A's right shoulder.

(**24**) 'Ding Dong' as they move in a sing song voice, then an immediate change into parents.

(**25**) Shamus can pull chorus A's arm down to eye level as he bends, and simultaneously A stretches his fingers and turns his palm to Shamus to make a peep hole.

(**26**) Jesus stands patiently as he is rebuffed. Shamus' tone of voice is extremely yob like. He bends his knees as if seated at a computer, and mimes playing an exciting game.
Make sure that the audience can believe in the computer. Facial expression reflecting successes and failures in the game will assist this.

Chorus C	(*To audience DSL*) One year comes, another goes,
Chorus B	(*To audience DSC*) Shamus is twelve before he knows. (**27**)
Chorus A	(*Moves to Shamus*) Aren't you a big boy then? (**28**)
Chorus B	(*Moves to Shamus*) Hasn't he grown?
Shamus	Shut up will you. Buzz off. GO. (**29**) I'm computing don't you know? My life I'm trying hard to win Machine code . . . Basic . . . I'm done in! Start again on dummy run It's exciting . . . It's *great* fun.
Chorus A, B, C	Ding Dong! (*Chorus A becomes door. Chorus B and C move USC*) (**30**) Shamus, answer the door! And be quick about it.
Jesus	(*Speaks in character as Abdu as Shamus opens door*) Please help me. I need some medicine for my son. (**31**)
Shamus	(*Sarcastically*) What do you think this is? A hospital? (**32**)
	(*All freeze*)
Narrator	(*Enters DSL*) Abdu is a resident of Katni, a small village in Bangladesh. The people, though very poor, are resilient and loving. The children learn early in life that although their parents can give them affection, they cannot always provide food. Abdu's eleven-year-old son is suffering from a severe case of intestinal worms. He may die . . . but Abdu has not enough money to buy treatment. (**33**)
Shamus	(*Coming back to life. Speaks dismissively*) Buy your own medicine.

(27)   Definitely approaching teenage awkwardness here, growing older before our very eyes!

(28)   As admiring relatives treating him as if he was five!

(29)   Shamus continues to play throughout. Emphasise the word 'life' as it has relevance later in the script, especially when Shamus loses his!

(30)   See (24).

(31)   Door as before. Jesus assumes the character of a Bangladeshi father. Don't attempt the accent unless it is really natural. The difference between Jesus and the other characters is that he is representing real life, so his acting must not be stylised in any way, in contrast to the others.

(32)   Address 'A hospital?' to the audience, as if expecting them to share the joke with him.

(33)   We must believe in this character. So the speech must be delivered with sincerity and feeling.

Jesus	(*As Abdu*) If I use my money for medicine my other children will starve. It's so hard to see him suffer and impossible to make the choice between his life and the lives of his brothers and sisters. Help us . . . please. (**34**)
Shamus	(*Leaning towards him angrily*) I haven't got anything to spare. Go away. (*Slams door and moves CS speaking to the audience*) One way of keeping the world population down.
	(*Narrator turns with back to audience*)
	(*Jesus as Abdu turns away sadly*)
	(*Shamus chews gum and mimes, listening to Walkman*) (**35**)
Chorus A	(DSL) Shamus in his teenage years . . . Fulfils all his mother's fears.
Chorus B	Hates his sister. (**36**)
	(*Shamus moves to Chorus ASL and grabs her threateningly*)
Chorus C	(*Moves CS towards Shamus*) Kicks her in.
	(*Shamus pushes Chorus A to the ground and mimes kicking*)
Chorus B	(*Moves DS speaking to audience*) Doesn't care that it's a sin.
Shamus	(*To Chorus A*) Excuse me. (*Kick*) Having a good time?
	(*Chorus A stands as door DSR*) (**37**)
	(*Jesus turns. Rings doorbell*)
	(*Narrator DSL. Turns to audience*)
Chorus A, B, C	Ding dong.
Shamus	(*Suspiciously opening door slightly. Impatiently*) Hello! (**38**)

(34)   Make sure that the air of desperation is evident, especially at the end of the speech. Don't gabble, use pauses to point the emotion. Don't over-dramatise!

(35)   Dance and rave as he listens to Walkman, oblivious of the speaking around him.

(36)   There must be no pause here as he grabs Chorus A and pushes him/her to the ground. He kicks here as part of his dance routine with great violence. Please stress that he is acting and not doing it 'for real' or you could have an emergency on your hands! The reaction of Chorus A is vital here as it must look as though there is some suffering!

(37)   As before.

(38)   Mime unlocking the door and use the arm as if opening the door. Chorus A turn as appropriate.

Jesus (*As the victim*) I'm a victim of torture from the government forces. I need you to protest about the conditions under which I and others live. We live rough in the sewers, and scavenge for food from the rubbish left by the rich. I have a brother and sister to care for. All I want is peace, and a place for us all to live. (**39**)

Shamus You should be so lucky!

(*All FREEZE*) (**40**)

Narrator Carla *is* lucky. She wasn't tortured or raped as many young people are. She wasn't electrocuted, burned or threatened with death. She wasn't even locked up without trial . . . She was just shot for being homeless and on the streets. She was shot, just once, whilst running away from the police. She lay on the ground, a bullet in her back, fired by an execution squad. Some say that such things only happen to terrorists. Carla is only ten years old. Many are younger. It's hard to believe these appalling examples of abuse until you have seen the scars. (**41**)

Shamus (*To Narrator*) Rubbish . . . It's all trumped up by the newspapers. Don't try to get *my* sympathy. Go on . . . on yer bike. (*Slams door. Moves USC*).

(*Jesus/Narrator. Both turn backs to audience*) (**42**)

(*Chorus B and C move SR to Chorus A*)

Chorus A (*To audience*) Now our Shamus . . . He's eighteen. Loud pop music is his scene.

Chorus A, B, C (*Singing as Spice Girls*) What I want, what I really, really, want. (**43**)

(*Shamus joins in and dances to CS leering at Chorus, and continues dancing through next dialogue*)

(**39**)   This character could be a Brazilian street child. Research into the problems suffered there is a must, so that the lines can be delivered with feeling.

(**40**)   Everyone should be involved in this and should be looking and reacting as human beings to the tale that is being told so that when frozen the reactions and thoughts communicate to the audience.

(**41**)   These facts must be delivered with feeling. And the lines *must* be learned. No excuses and scrappy bits of paper!

(**42**)   The turn and the move should take place simultaneously or the action will be slowed down.

(**43**)   Just one or two lines of the song will be enough to make the point, but the group need to work out definite 'Spice Girl' movements with exaggerated abandon. Don't just improvise, work it out in detail. Shamus could join in if that feels right!

Chorus B   (*Walking past Shamus to USL hands over ears*) Shamus! Turn it down. (**44**)

Shamus   NO.

Chorus C   (*Walking past Shamus to USL hands over ears*) Shamus! Your mother needs some help.

Shamus   So what? (**45**)

Chorus A   (*Taps his shoulder*) Shamus! Your sister's just been run over by a bus. (**46**)

Shamus   (*Still freaking out*) TOUGH!

(*Chorus A shakes head and moves USCL*)

Chorus B   (*Turns and steps forward*) Shamus! Don't you care about anyone? (**47**)

Shamus   (*Moves and grabs Chorus B, pretends to head butt*) Yes . . . ME!

Chorus C   (*Moves between them and separates them. Moves DSR*) For selfish Shamus, life goes on. (**48**)

(*Shamus. Move USC and join arms with B as if going down the aisle. Chorus A becomes bridesmaid and follows them*) (**49**)

Chorus A, B, C   (*Sing Wedding March as Shamus and B move DSCL*) Da da da dah, Da da da dah!

Chorus A   (*Moves DSL. Seriously to audience*) He's married now.

Chorus A, B, C   At twenty-one. (**50**)

Chorus C   (*To audience*) Thinks his life has just begun.

Chorus B   (*Step back one step*) Years roll by . . . he's thirty (*Step back*) . . . forty. (**51**)

(*Jesus rings bell*)

(44)   Shout angrily here as if over the music.

(45)   With a sneer and total unconcern.

(46)   Spoken with a smile, in a cheerful voice.

(47)   Shocked tone of voice.

(48)   As storyteller.

(49)   Chorus B links arms with Shamus CS as bride and groom, Chorus A moves behind as bridesmaid.

(50)   As people at a party celebrating and raising glasses.

(51)   Should be fairly central and the steps must be positive as they symbolise the passing of time. As each age is mentioned, Shamus grows older.

(*Chorus C becomes door*) (**52**)

Chorus A, B, C   Ding dong.

Chorus A   Shamus! Answer the door. (**53**)

Shamus   (*Sighs reluctantly*) Oh! All right.

Jesus   (*As Shamus opens door*) I'm in prison because of my faith. Pray for me.

Shamus   What do you mean . . . pray for you? (**54**)

(*All FREEZE*)

Narrator   (*Turns to audience*) Pastor Yeng has already been in prison for his Christian beliefs for six years. The authorities told him that if he denied his faith he'd be free. He refuses. He was guilty only of caring for his flock, members of a secret house church in China. He cannot get medical treatment for his rheumatoid arthritis. He is isolated. He cannot have visitors, and fears for the lives of his wife and three children. There are many others who, because of their beliefs are imprisoned, or held hostage, or persecuted by different political regimes all over the world.

Jesus   (*As Pastor Yeng*) I will not deny my faith. I will work for the right of all to have freedom of thought and conscience. It's so very hard to keep going. It's only the knowledge that my brothers and sisters pray for me and act on my behalf when I am helpless, and the love of my God, which keeps me alive in the face of hostility (**55**)

Shamus   Look! (*Impatiently*) I'm a bit busy. The wife is busy, the dog is busy, the cat is busy . . .(*angrily*) and even the goldfish is busy! (*Nonchalantly*) Can't spare the time to worry about your problems. I've got enough of my own. Bye. (*Shuts door firmly and moves US back to audience*) (**56**)

(*Jesus looks at him sadly*)

(*Narrator exits DSL*)

(**52**)   As before.

(**53**)   As nagging wife. Shamus looks henpecked and slouches towards the door.

(**54**)   Absolutely astonished at the thought!

(**55**)   See notes about other characters portrayed by Jesus.

(**56**)   The timing of this speech is important. Really 'attack' the words, and build up to the anger. Then change mood at the end and look pleased to have got rid of this 'door to door salesman'.

Chorus B	(*Step back*) Fifty. (**57**)
	(*Jesus rings bell*)
Chorus A, B, C	Ding dong.
Shamus	(*Turns and marches to the door*) This is ridiculous. Look, how many times do I have to tell you that I don't want you coming round disturbing my peace. This is *my* house. You're *not* coming in. I'm *not* helping you. I've too many important things to do. (**58**)
Chorus B	Sixty.
	(*Jesus rings bell*)
Chorus A, B, C	Ding dong (*Chorus A moves USCL. Chorus C moves to Chorus B CS and both turn backs to audience*) (**59**)
	(*Jesus turns back on Shamus*) (**60**)
Shamus	Seventy. (*Moves DCS as old man*) Eighty-five. Eeeeeee . . . I do feel tired. (*He dies spectacularly*) (**61**)
	(*Chorus A, B and C turn as cleaning ladies*) (**62**)
Chorus B	You do the stairs and I'll do the floor Ada. (*Kneels DSL with bucket and cloth. Mime*) (**63**)
Chorus C	OK Ethel. (*Walks US and then down as if cleaning. Sees body and reacts in shock*) 'Ere! 'Ere Ethel . . . look at this. (*pointing at Shamus*) (**64**)
Chorus B	Oh dear, Doris. (*Kneeling beside him and taking his pulse, etc.*) How long do you think it's been here?
Chorus A	(*Picks up an arm which is rigid, and stays upright when she lets it go*) A day or so I'd say. (**65**)
Chorus C	I feel dizzy, Ethel. It's the shock! I don't like dead bodies. (*Moves DSCR*) They make me come over all faint. (*Thinks*) Makes you wonder though. (**66**)
Chorus B	Wonder about what, Ada?

(57)   Age a little more and freeze in character.

(58)   Extremely angry, but remember your age! This should be reflected in the way that you move.

(59)   Move as 'ding dong' is sung out. Slick and quick is the key!

(60)   This must be a definite and strong move.

(61)   At each age Shamus must appear to shrink, until he seems very frail, perhaps miming a walking stick, and shaking hand. Make each change definite. Make the most of the death. Sway and stagger, fall to knees, moan and finally end flat on back with legs in the air. Slowly let the legs go down on a final moan.

(62)   The three cleaning ladies need to be stereotypes preferably with broad accents. They should be very different from any character before. It would be excellent if they had different physical characteristics. E.g. one nervous, the others confident? They must not appear to see the body at first.

(63)   Some work on mime would be useful. There is nothing worse than 'wafty' mime, with objects changing size and shape. Make sure that the bucket has weight and the details of wringing out the cloth, etc. are realistic. Working with real objects first can help, but they can't be used in performance as it wouldn't fit in with the style of the sketch.

(64)   Doris is the confident one, and is not at all put out by seeing a body, just curious. She'll enjoy having a bit of a gossip about this, it'll keep her going when she next goes 'down the pub'! Ethel is more sensitive, and nervous about the whole thing, and this must show in the way she nervously takes the pulse.

(65)   Shamus must keep his arm rigid until he becomes a ghost.

(66)   Very puzzled, and addresses the audience, as if taking them into her confidence.

Chorus C	Well . . . I always wonder where we go when we die.
Chorus B	Eeeeeee, Ada! (**67**)

(*Chorus A moving DSL Coming out of Cleaning lady characters*) *Shamus lying in his coffin.* (**68**)

Chorus A, B, C	(*To audience, sadly*) All that's left of his life is . . . (*Pause*) nothing. (**69**)

(*Ghost noises*) (**70**)

(*Shamus rises as a ghost and moves DSR*)

(*Chorus A, B, C turn with backs to Shamus in a diagonal line*)

(*Jesus moves across to Chorus A, B, C, D, and turns with back to Shamus*) (**71**)

Shamus	(*Knocking on Jesus' back*) Hello! Is this heaven? It's Shamus here. Remember me? We met before, at my front door. We had a chat. Remember that? Well, you said you'd call again another day. Remember when? (*Shouting rudely, as if to a deaf person*) HELLO! IT'S SHAMUS! (**72**)

(*Chorus A, B, C, turn slowly and gaze at him sadly*) (**73**)

Jesus	(*Turns slowly and looks Shamus in the eye*) I was hungry and you did not feed me. (**74**) I was thirsty and you gave me nothing to drink. I was naked and you did not clothe me. I was in prison and you did not visit me. I never knew you. (*Turns his back*)

(*Chorus A, B, C, turn away from him*)

Shamus	(*Backs away, writhes in agony and sinks to the floor*) No . . . I didn't think . . . there wasn't time . . . Aaaaaaaaaaaargh! (**75**)

(*All FREEZE*) (**76**)

(67)   Another immediate change into story tellers.

(68)   They stand as if at a funeral. Tone of voice . . . doom laden!

(69)   Put a greater emphasis on the word 'nothing'.

(70)   As the Chorus make ghost noises, you'll have to experiment with these – sorry! Shamus rises and moves as floating ghost, joining in with the wailing.

(71)   It is best if Jesus moves as the ghost noises begin, a ray of dignity and sanity amongst farce!

(72)   This is an echo of the door situation motif, and the tenor of the sketch becomes suddenly more serious as we realise that Shamus has 'blown it'. It helps if Shamus is quite confident that he is to be let in, after all he's had is own way all his life?

(73)   The slow turn and the eye contact are important, as is a slight pause before Jesus says what we expect!

(74)   This must be delivered quite sternly but not angrily. It is important that the images of the needy we have met during the scene are remembered at this point.

(75)   This is quite difficult to do, and for the first time Shamus must be human and realistic in order to make the point. If it raises a laugh, it will be a mockery. So a bit of realistic dramatic acting here please.

(76)   Hold the FREEZE for about 5 seconds. Chorus A, B and C and Jesus should have their backs to Shamus and be standing firm, with feet slightly apart to give a look of strength and of course good balance.

Heavenly Love
Background

CHARACTERS

Chorus A/Mum/
1st Girl
Originally played by a girl, but might be funny as a male!

Chorus B/Cashier/
2nd Girl
Needs to be a stereotypical efficient, reliable secretary, and works best with a girl, especially as she is also the potential girlfriend of the Prodigal.

Chorus C/Mum/
3rd Girl
Originally played by a girl, but again might be funny as a male!

Prodigal
Versatility required and a sense of comedy and pathos. Better played as a male, but a girl might get away with it.

APPROACH

- This sketch is a mixture of styles, and requires pace and attack.

- Study and discussion about the parable of the Lost Son is vital prior to staging in order to get the message over.

- Improvisations around aspects of the sketch would be useful.

- The essence is comedy with a serious message about the Forgiveness of God and his forgiveness.

- It works well with older teenagers.

- I recommend that this sketch is performed after working on some of the others in this book, unless the actors are experienced.

Heavenly Love
(Luke 18:15-24)

Starting Positions

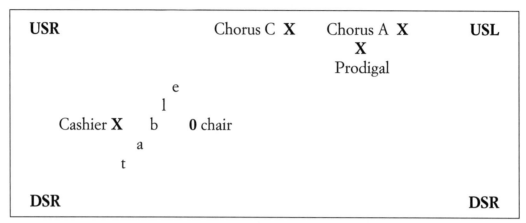

(*The stage is set with a table CSR. Sitting at the desk is an efficient female cashier. USCL with backs to the audience are the other characters.*) (**1**)

Chorus A	Brrrr. Brrr. Brrrr. Brrr. (**2**)
Cashier	(*Answering the phone*) The Heavenly Build It On *Love* Society . . . Can I help you? . . . Yes sir . . . that's fine. (*Puts phone down. Loudly*) NEXT! (**3**)
Customer	(*As Customer. Moves to stand to left of chair CSR, angrily shaking umbrella in mime.*) I hate this stupid rain! I hate this stupid umbrella. These shoes let the water in . . . it's *terrible*! (**4**)
Cashier	(*Interrupting cheerfully*) Can I help you?
Customer	(*Sitting*) Yes. I want to draw some love out please. I'm at the end of my tether. (*She glares*) (**5**)
Cashier	Well . . . how much would you like?
Customer	(*Still extremely angry*) About a week's worth please!

Director's tips

(1)   The cashier is seated to the right of the table, sitting diagonally, with pencil in hand, making notes. The others have their backs to the audience standing relaxed in NEUTRAL.

(2)   If the sound is not loud enough Chorus B and C can do it also, but make sure that it is synchronised.

(3)   All the action is in mime. The telephone is indicated by putting the right thumb to the right ear, curling the first three fingers toward the palm, and the little finger stretched towards the mouth. Remember when using the 'phone' to allow pauses to listen to the person speaking on the other end of the line!

(4)   The customer is obviously in a bad temper, and in this instance may use an umbrella if desired, otherwise make sure that the mime is believable and accurate.

(5)   Make sure that the chair she sits on is facing downstage and not towards SR to enable the audience to see her facial expressions. Emphasise the word 'love' at all times.

Cashier	A week's worth . . . Would you sign on the dotted line please? Thank you. (**6**)
Customer	I hate filling in these stupid forms. I hate this signature.
Cashier	(*Politely*) How would you like your love?
Customer	Three 'I love you's and a loving heart please.
Cashier	There you are Madam. Have a *lovely* day! (*C moves back to USC with a big beaming smile*) (**7**)
Chorus C	Good morning. *Lovely* day! (*To Prodigal who grumpily waits his turn.*) (**8**)
Cashier	Next!
Prodigal	(*In a great hurry, rudely*) I want to draw out all the love I've got on account. (**9**)
Cashier	(*Shocked*) Pardon! (**10**)
Prodigal	(*Sulkily*) I want all the love in my account . . . *now*! (**11**)
Cashier	(*Very concerned*) But, Sir . . . what about your *Life* Assurance?
Prodigal	(*Irritated*) I don't care about that. (*Angry*) I want all my love. (*Extremely angry*) And I want it NOW! (**12**)
Cashier	(*Patronisingly*) You do realise that your account will be automatically closed, and you will have no love left. All the work I do on *your* behalf will be wasted! (**13**)
Prodigal	(*Petulantly*) I want my share of love NOW! (**14**)
Cashier	(*Icily*) Excuse me, please . . . (*Dials on phone*) Hello! Could you put me through to Mr Carpenter Senior, please . . . Hello, sir. I have a man here who wants to draw out all his love . . . yes . . . that's what I told him . . . and I told him about his Life Assurance, sir . . . Oh? (*Looks at the phone in amazement*) . . . yes . . . I know it's his by right, but . . . Right, sir. As you say, sir. (*Peremptorily*) How would you like your love? (**15**) (**16**)

(6) The cashier goes into 'highly efficient' mode as she pushes a paper to the customer who picks up the pen and signs irritatedly.

(7) As the customer moves back he/she holds out her hand to check for rain and on seeing that it has stopped beams even more.

(8) Prodigal turns, looking at his watch, impatient for his turn. Acknowledge Prodigal who is the next client. He ignores the acknowledgement.

(9) The Prodigal must stride to the seat impatiently and sit in the same manner. He has obviously run out of love all together!

(10) The Cashier's tone of voice as she says 'pardon' must imply criticism of his attitude.

(11) A thump on the table to emphasise 'now' works well especially if it makes the cashier jump. Make sure that the facial expressions and the body language of the Prodigal communicate his mood.

(12) This line should be delivered in three sharp bursts with the last one at the peak of his anger. The Cashier is obviously shocked and irritated by his general behaviour. Reaction to others is vital in any piece of drama.

(13) Gathers herself together and is pointedly patronising. Careful and deliberate enunciation can emphasise this even further.

(14) As a spoiled child with a whining voice and an extremely sulky expression, in reaction to the now patronising attitude of the Cashier.

(15) This is quite a difficult speech. Remember to use pauses and listen to the other end of the conversation. It is useful to imagine exactly what is being said. The Cashier represents the brother in the story, the one who is always there! There must be shock apparent at what she is being told to do. Occasional glances of dislike towards the Prodigal also helps to communicate this idea.

(16) Think of the Prodigal's attitude to the conversation. He might drum his fingers on the table impatiently and have an 'I told you so' expression by the end of it.

Prodigal	(*With a self-satisfied smile*) Worldly love, self love and romantic love.
Cashier	(*To Prodigal*) Sign on the dotted line . . . thank you. (*Disparagingly*) There you are, sir.
Prodigal	(*Triumphantly*) I *love* it when I get what I want! (*Moves CSL*) (**17**)
Cashier	(*Sarcastically*) Have a lovely day, sir. (**18**)
	(*Mum moves CS becomes 'Mum'*)
Prodigal	(*Wheedling voice*). Mum? Er can I have some money for one of those . . . (**19**)
Mum	(*Crossly*) You had one of those yesterday.
Prodigal	Aw Mum!
Mum	(*Sighing*) *And* you had one last week, not to mention last Sunday. You must think I'm made of money.
Prodigal	(*Offended*) Mum . . . I don't! (*Wheedling voice*) I'll tell you something though. I really *love* you. (**20**)
Mum	(*With a pleased smirk*) Oh! . . . Go on then. (*Turn and freeze*) (**21**)
Prodigal	(*Moves DSC*)
Friend	(*Moves DSC to left of Prodigal*) Hi, Andy! How are you? (**22**)
Prodigal	(*Exaggerated*) Starving.
Friend	I am as well.
Prodigal	(*Enthusiastically*) Let's get something to eat.
Friend	(*Sadly*) Well I can't. I've no money! (*Hopefully*) Have you? (**23**)

(**17**)   Exaggerated triumph to both the Cashier and the audience.

(**18**)   Chorus C turns and move CS swiftly. Cashier stands with back to audience.

(**19**)   As a spoilt child with a wheedling voice.

(**20**)   Putting arm around her with definite signs of 'cupboard love'!

(**21**)   Giving him a peck on the cheek before turning on the spot with back to audience and resuming NEUTRAL stance.

(**22**)   Very enthusiastic at seeing Prodigal. This is important in order to contrast more effectively with the reaction later after the Prodigal's selfish treatment. He is obviously misunderstanding the true meaning of 'love'!

(**23**)   This next sequence assumes that the shop is in the audience and so all the action is directed out front. The Friend must show through body language and facial expression how hungry she is. It must make the audience have a 'mouth-watering' experience, and they must empathise with the Friend.

Prodigal	(*Boasting*) I have. I got some out of my mum. (*Moves as if to assistant in shop*) Ooooh, I love those. I'll have one, please!
Friend	(*Pleading*) Two?
Prodigal	(*Ignoring her. Speaking to imaginary shop assistant*) Cor! I love them I'll have one of those too. (*Eating with great enjoyment*) (**24**)
Friend	(*Trying again persuasively*) Two?
Prodigal	(*Ignoring her. Speaking again to imaginary shop assistant*) And I *love* them! I'll have *two* of them. (**24**)
Friend	(*Expectantly*) Great! (**25**)
Prodigal	Mmmmmmm . . . (*Eating exuberantly. Walking away from her*) I really love these. (*Takes another large bite*) Gorgeous. Mmmmmmmmmmmm! (**26**)
Friend	(*Following and watching with mouth watering*) I'm starving!
Prodigal	(*Waving it under her nose*) You should try this; it's fantastic! (**27**)
Friend	(*Upset and angry*) Thank you . . . and GOODBYE! (*Turn and FREEZE*)
Prodigal	(*Looking in mirror DSC*) I am *so* good looking. I reckon my hair is really trendy. Shouldn't have much problem getting a good-looking girl. Where are you, you *lucky* woman? (**28**)

(*Chorus A, Chorus B and Chorus C turn and group round him*) (**29**)

Hi, girls! Do you fancy me?

(*All Chorus. Giggle*) |

(24)   There is a total disregard for her feelings as the Prodigal chews and licks his lips in enjoyment. The Friend's reaction should be as a child watching someone take away a special treat.

(25)   A look of delight at the thought of food.

(26)   A really disappointed expression here continues as the prodigal greedily eats.

(27)   The Friend is almost in tears with frustration at this point.

(28)   This is a really narcissistic speech. Take time over it, put plenty of hair combing and straightening of clothes, and any other 'trendy' behaviour as he looks in the mirror and admires himself. This should be funny and get an audience reaction!

(29)   Cashier becomes 3rd girl and crosses to Prodigal in front of table. The others turn at the same time and become as giggling girls who fancy a pop star.

Prodigal	I am the best player in the football team. You should see me score! The crowd only comes to see my style! Everybody loves me. (**30**)
1st Girl	(*Excited*) Guess what! I went to see a . . . (**31**)
Prodigal	(*Interrupting rudely*) I've just bought some new clothes. Aren't they ace! Don't you love them? (*Preening himself*) Of course it's the fella inside that makes them so eye catching! Lovely aren't they?
2nd Girl	(*Excited*) I bought a new dress the other day . . . (**32**)
Prodigal	(*Rudely interrupting*) So what? (*Boasting*) I got a new red sports car. Just suits my macho personality. (*Smirking nonchalantly*) I love that car. I love speeding down the motorway more than anything else in the world!
1st Girl	(*Accusingly*) You're too full of yourself! (*Turn*) (**33**)
3rd Girl	(*Sarcastically*) Love yourself don't you? (*Turn*) (**33**)
2nd Girl	(*Annoyed*) Oh, talk to yourself. (*Turn*) (**33**)
Prodigal	Go away . . . you're boring! (*To audience*) I want to tell you something. I met a girl last week . . . And I think I'm in love. I really want to tell her, but . . . (**34**)
3rd Girl	(*Shyly*) Hiya Andy. (**35**)
Prodigal	(*Really thrilled, but a little shy.*) Hiya . . . I'm so glad you're here, I've got something important to tell you. I really need to tell you . . . (**36**)
3rd Girl	(*Expectantly*) Yes?
Prodigal	(*Gazing at her adoringly*) I've realised over the last week that I really l, l, l . . . I really, really, l . . . (**37**)
3rd Girl	(*Gazing at him adoringly*) Are you trying to tell me something?

(30)   This sequence must be played with pace, and the Prodigal must be extremely self-satisfied and boastful, also rude, in order to change the girls' opinion of him by the end of the sequence. He doesn't really listen to anything they say, thinking only of himself. Much 'Cool dude' behaviour and body language here too!

(31)   Her face falls, hurt, as she is interrupted.

(32)   See (31).

(33)   These lines must be delivered with attack and feeling. As each one finishes speaking they turn with back to audience and take one step upstage.

(34)   This is the first time he appears to be sincere, and the audience must feel sympathy for him as he displays early teenage angst!

(35)   Really exaggerated shyness, and it must be obvious that she likes him a lot as this points his inability to use any more 'love'.

(36)   They gaze at each other, moonstruck for a moment.

(37)   The 'I' must get stuck in his throat as he makes a real effort to tell her he loves her. This is the key to the meaning of the sketch, that he has been given everything he asked for and has misused and wasted it. He is desperate and miserable.

Prodigal	Yes! I want you to know that I really (*Having great difficulty in getting his words out*) 1, 1, 1 . . . I can't say it! (**38**)
3rd Girl	(*Embarrassed*) This is stupid.
Prodigal	But I really 1, 1, 1, 1, 1 . . .
3rd Girl	Oh. Forget it! (*Moves back to table and stands with back to audience*) (**39**)
Prodigal	(*Confidentially to audience*) I've just seen her. I, I, I couldn't tell her. The words just wouldn't come out. I'm sorry. I didn't mean to be selfish. I didn't mean to make everyone hate me. I hate you. I hate life. I hate everything!
Chorus A, Chorus C	(*Turn together*) You've run out of love. (**40**)
Prodigal	(*Miserably*) I've run out of 1, 1, 1, 1, 1, 1 . . .
Chorus A, Chorus C	(*Together*) LOVE! (**41**)
Cashier	Next!
Prodigal	(*Tentatively*) I'd like to draw out some 1 . . . (**42**)
Cashier	(*Officiously*) Oh it's *you* is it? I informed you last time you came in that if you drew out all our love your account would be closed! (**43**)
Prodigal	I don't suppose there's any love to spare?
Cashier	(*Interrupting him, extremely irritated*) I've worked on your behalf for a number of years, and I do not intend to wear myself into the ground in order to help you out. (*Belligerently*) YOU haven't any love left!
Prodigal	(*Penitently*) I'm really sorry. I know I've done some terrible things. I know I've wasted everything, lost all my friends, but . . .

(38)   By this point he is terribly upset, and sinks to his knees. The girl looks on in amazement and embarrassment.

(39)   He puts his head in his hands, and then for the first time begins to speak as a human being, directly to the audience who should feel sorry for him. The speech should engender pathos.

(40)   Patronisingly.

(41)   Leaning towards him as they speak, and then turning with backs to the audience and moving slightly further upstage into neutral position. Chorus B becomes cashier and sits at the table.

(42)   He moves very hesitantly and slides shamefaced into his seat obviously expecting a rebuff.

(43)   She enjoys every minute as the Prodigal squirms in his seat.

Chorus A	Brrrr. Brrr. Brrrr. Brrr.
Cashier	(*Answering the phone*) Yes sir . . . Yes he's here. (*amazed*) You saw him coming?
Prodigal	(*Loudly and sincerely*) I'm *really* sorry! (**44**)
Cashier	Erm . . . Do you mind! Yes, sir . . . he says he's sorry sir. (*Pause as a look of incredulity appears on her face*) *Pardon*, sir? (*Pause*) *Your* love, sir? (*Pause*) Give him *all* of it, sir? (*Pause*) Re-open his account! Well, sir . . . if you don't mind my saying so, sir, I think it's a liberty . . . it *is* sir! (*Pause*) All right, sir! . . . You're sure. Right, sir. (*Embarrassed and irritated*) The manager says that (*Cough nervously*) you can have his love. So your account is now full . . . to overflowing. (**45**)
Prodigal	(*Incredulously*) He's given me *His* love? (**46**)
Cashier	(*Icily. Polite*) Yes, sir. That's right. You're permanently in credit. No debts.
Prodigal	(*Amazed*) I can have *His* love. Does that mean I can draw some out?
Cashier	(*Icily. Polite*) How much would that be?
Prodigal	(*Thinks*) About an hour's worth?
Cashier	(*Politely*) How would you like your love?
Prodigal	I don't know.
Cashier	(*Efficiently*) Make your mark with a *cross* . . . just here.
Prodigal	(*Puzzled*) A cross?
Cashier	(*Cheerfully*) There you are, sir. One I love you, one river of the water of life, forgiveness of sins, and the promise of eternal life.
Prodigal	(*Shamefaced to audience*) I don't deserve all this.

(44) Leaning towards the telephone as he shouts. The cashier leans away from him.

(45) See previous note about the mime telephone. This is worth spending some time on as it represents the homecoming of the prodigal and the forgiveness he is given, also the attitude of the brother is reflected in the attitude of the cashier. Keep this in mind.

(46) The following dialogue, speaks for itself, as long as both remain in character and think about the emotions and feelings which must have been experienced by the lost son in the parable, and the jealousy of his brother. Keep it flowing, with clear diction and with feeling.

Cashier   (*Firmly*) You certainly don't, sir! (*Politely*) But that's the package; take it or leave it!

Prodigal   I'll take it! Thank you. Thank you (*Moves to Chorus A and C*) (**47**)

Cashier   (*Dials phone. Angrily*) This is ridiculous. I sit here every day of the week, a big smile on my face, handing out love to people like there's no tomorrow. (*Self righteously*) Have I complained? Have I complained? No! (*Angrily*) Well I'm complaining now. I've never been given anything like that. (*Offended*) And *he* doesn't even work here. (*Pause. Change of tone*) Right. (*Pause*) well (*Pause*) Pardon? (*Pause*) Pardon? (*Crossly*) I beg your pardon. (*Pause. Mockingly*) I am always here with you? You can say that again! You fill his account with love, to overflowing. And what do I get? (*Pause. Puzzled*) Dead? *Dead?* But he's alive . . . What do you mean '*precisely*'? (*Pause. Even more puzzled*) Lost? *Lost?* (*Pause*) Found? (*Irritated*) Yes, some people always land on their feet (*Pause. Amazed*) You mean it's the same for me too? (*Somewhat pacified*) Well . . . that's all right then! (*Politely*) Goodbye, sir! (*Pause. Pleased*) What? A *party*? (*Pause. Horrified*) . . . at *my* house? (**48**)

(*FREEZE*) (**49**)

(**47**)   As he reaches them, Chorus A and B turn communicating renewed friendship, with the Prodigal indicating with a gesture the place where his forgiveness has come from. The others react in joy. They make a QUICK PIC of joy and friendship. FREEZE until the end of the sketch, so make it positions which can be held for a while as the focus must not be drawn from the Cashier.

(**48**)   A variety of emotions are shown in this speech, and it is useful to discuss them with the group and for the person playing the character to write in the reasons for each change of tone and reaction, in the script. The speech goes from self-righteous anger, to calm, to polite sarcasm, to shock, etc. Don't be afraid to listen to the other end. Perhaps an improvised session with someone playing Mr Carpenter Senior might help.

(49)   Hold the FREEZE for 3-5 seconds, including all facial expressions.

NB: An alternative ending would be if Prodigal breaks away from his group, and Cashier moves towards him and you decide whether they would shake hands, or whether the cashier would turn away? or you can leave the original ending and let the audience work it out. That's what we decided to do!

Glossary

Aside
A comment made deliberately to the audience, but which is apparently not heard by other characters on stage. Alternatively, a comment which is made to another character on stage and excludes others. It is very much apparent in the melodramatic style where audience participation was encouraged.

Blocking
Roughly planning out the moves within the stage area, and pencilling them in the script. Be flexible, they may have to be changed.

CS
(Centre Stage) A position right in the centre of the acting area.

CSL
(Centre Stage Left) A position a little to the left of the centre of the acting area.

CSR
(Centre Stage Right) A position a little to the right of the centre of the acting area.

Cue
A word or visual signal of some kind which indicates either a reaction or another move or response from an actor or technician.

DSC
(Down Stage Centre) A position in the middle at the front of the acting area nearest to the audience.

DSCL
(Down Stage Centre Left) A position at the front of the acting area left of centre.

DSCR
(Down Stage Centre Right) A position at the front of the acting area right of centre.

DSL
(Down Stage Left) A position at the extreme left of the acting area, at the front, nearest the audience.

DSR
(Down Stage Right) A position at the extreme right of the acting area, at the front, nearest the audience.

Focus
1 The words or actions upon which you wish the audience to concentrate.

2 The concentrated attitude of the actor bent upon his task, without being distracted.

3 The highest physical point of energy of an action.

Freeze
Suspended animation, total stillness, usually focused on a point of energy.

Freeze Frame
Suspended animation of a group of actors, rather like the 'stills' in a film sequence.

Improvisation   To develop a scene or character without a script, often spontaneously.

Levels   A series of positions in the acting area, which places the actors in a visually interesting position in relation one to another and also creates focus, and reveals status in their relationships as characters.

Masking   One actor standing in front of another and preventing the audience from seeing or focusing where they should.

Mime   Action without words.

Neutral   This involves standing still and relaxed, with feet slightly apart, to give good balance. When in neutral there should be a stillness, and a sense of just being there without making any statement to distract from the action. Complete stillness and relaxation is the order of the day. It's a bit like the breathing and relaxation in an upright position!

Polished Improvisation   An improvisation which has been worked on and edited prior to scripting.

Quick Pics   A small frozen group tableau representing a scene, situation or idea.

SL   *(Stage Left)* A position to the extreme left of the centre of the acting area.

SR   *(Stage Right)* A position to the extreme right of the centre of the acting area.

Stage Directions

93

Tableau   A still group picture.

USC   *(Up Stage Centre)* A position at the centre back of the acting area.

USCL   *(Up Stage Centre Left)* A position at the back of the acting area and slightly to the left.

USCR   *(Up Stage Centre Right)* A position at the back of the acting area and slightly to the right when facing the audience.

USL   *(Up Stage Left)* A position at the back of the acting area to the extreme left of centre, when facing the audience.

USR   *(Up Stage Right)* A position at the back of the acting area to the extreme right of centre, when facing the audience.

WIP   *(Walking Into Pictures)* An exercise where the whole group creates a picture, as if in a frame on a given theme, concentrating on relationships between the actors within their situation. It must be an interesting visual communication. It must accurately communicate the theme, and show thoughtfulness by the actors in terms of their positioning and levels and their sensitivity to the action and mime of others.

L9 1012